Fundamentals of Petroleum

Second Edition

Published by
PETROLEUM EXTENSION SERVICE
The University of Texas at Austin
Austin, Texas
1981

Contents

Foreword

Our nation cannot live without energy. Oil and natural gas provide about 70 percent of the energy used in the United States. Because of its importance, people directly related to and affected by this industry should know more about it. The better people understand the petroleum industry, the greater the chances are for making the proper decisions toward solutions to our energy problems.

The petroleum industry is a leader in developing and applying advanced technology. The Association of Desk and Derrick Clubs recognizes the need for a better understanding of this complex and diversified technology and endorses *Fundamentals of Petroleum*, which is dedicated to individuals seeking knowledge of the petroleum industry. Designed for both the professional and layman as a basic guide on the practical aspects of the petroleum industry, this book is intended to be used by the association as a primary text for training in house, in junior colleges, and through correspondence courses. It is also intended to serve as an educational tool for allied industries, as well as professional and governmental agencies. It provides under one cover a basic discussion of the petroleum industry, from geology and reservoirs through exploration, drilling, production, pipelining, refining, and marketing.

Fundamentals of Petroleum was developed from an idea proposed by Loretta Owens of the Desk and Derrick Club of Fort Worth, Texas, and further stimulated by the Desk and Derrick Club of Corpus Christi, Texas. Under the leadership of Ms. Owens, a committee, representing eight geographical locations within the association, developed and presented an outline to Petroleum Extension Service of The University of Texas at Austin. With these guidelines, the Petroleum Extension Service staff researched, developed, and published this training manual.

Desk and Derrick is a unique organization of over eight thousand members employed in the petroleum and allied industries who are dedicated to the proposition that *greater knowledge* of the petroleum industry will result in *greater service* through job performance. Nonshareholding, noncommercial, nonprofit, nonpartisan, and nonbargaining in its policies, the organization has very positive concepts on the value of education for women.

Association of Desk and Derrick Clubs
411 Thompson Building
Tulsa, Oklahoma 74103

Preface

fundamentals of Petroleum is designed to give an overall view of the petroleum industry in terms that are understandable by the layman as well as the professional. This manual does not cover all procedures and equipment used in the industry, nor does it give detailed descriptions of techniques used by oil and gas workers in the field. Rather, the authors and editors, mindful of its purpose, tried to include positive, useful information while minimizing technical material.

A companion to this text is the Fundamentals of Petroleum Correspondence Course coordinated by the Petroleum Extension Service, Austin office. The course uses *Fundamentals of Petroleum,* Second Edition, and a *Study Guide* based on the text. The course consists of ten lessons and a test.

Helpful supplements to this text are the *Desk and Derrick Oil Abbreviator,* available from Petroleum Publishing Company, Tulsa, Oklahoma, and *A Dictionary of Petroleum Terms,* available from Petroleum Extension Service, Austin, Texas. These will help the reader understand the petroleum language.

Based on a suggested outline from the Association of Desk and Derrick Clubs, this book was researched and compiled by Annes McCann and Martine Stemerick of the Petroleum Extension Service staff. Content consultants were Ron Baker; W. E. Boyd; O. L. Jacobs; Drew Laughlin; W. L. Ledgerwood, Jr.; D. W. McCarthy; Dennis Pugh; Doug Stuart; Clem L. Ware, CPL; Mark A. Welsh, Jr.; and Bruce R. Whalen. Staff artist Mark Donaldson was responsible for the cover graphics, and many of the illustrations. The final publishing was accomplished with the help of Vivian Carmona-Agosto, Deborah Caples, Cinda Cyrus, Martha Greenlaw, Terry Gregston, Donna Hankey, Paula Lawson, Glenn Moeller, Jane Sullivan, and Marion Vose.

We hope this effort will meet the needs of the members of the Desk and Derrick Clubs and people everywhere who are interested in petroleum. Their quest for knowledge is admirable and stimulating to our staff whose job is to develop training materials and schools for the petroleum industry.

Mildred Gerding
Editor

Acknowledgments

t he knowledge and talents of many persons and the resources of many organizations were utilized to produce this manual. The creative support provided by the individuals involved is gratefully acknowledged. Also, sincere appreciation is extended to the following companies and organizations for their generous contributions to this effort:

American Gas Association
American Petroleum Institute, Photographic and Film Services
Amoco Chemicals Corporation
Amoco Public and Government Affairs Department
Ana-Log, Inc.
ARCO Chemical Company
Brown & Root, Inc.
Cities Service Company
Coastal States Gas Corporation
Continental Pipe Line Company
El Paso Natural Gas Company
Exxon Pipeline Company
Federal Energy Regulatory Commission
Geosource Inc.
Interstate Natural Gas Association of America
Lunar and Planetary Institute
McGraw-Hill Book Company
Mitchell Energy & Development Corporation
Mobil Oil Corporation
Natural Gas Pipeline Company of America
Nicklos Drilling Corporation
Panhandle Eastern Pipe Line Company
Petroleum Publishing Company
Pertamina
Phillips Petroleum Company
Saber Energy Company
The Scott Petty Company
Standard Oil Company of California
Texaco, Inc.
Texas Eastern Transmission Corporation
Texas Gas Transmission Corporation
Transco

Petroleum Geology and Reservoirs

g eology is so essential to the petroleum industry that a knowledge of the basic principles of this science is desirable for anyone associated with oil or gas. Thus, an introduction to the petroleum industry should start with a brief outline of the geological processes, the origin and accumulation of petroleum, and how these concepts relate to the production of oil and gas.

Geology is the science that deals with the history and structure of the earth and its life forms, especially as recorded in the rocks. Rock is a natural substance composed of a mineral or group of minerals. The rocks that are of most interest to the petroleum geologist are those that contain fluids—fluids such as salt water, oil, or gas.

Geology is based on observation and knowledge derived from many other sciences. A first principle is that *the present is the key to the past,* which means that processes acting on the earth today are very similar to those that operated in the past. The geologist acquires basic information by observing rocks and their relationship to each other as they were formed in the layers of the earth. He then tries to reconstruct the events that gave rise to certain rock formations. From their arrangement, a petroleum geologist can sometimes predict where oil accumulations might occur.

For enough oil and gas to accumulate to form a commercially valuable deposit, there must be a reservoir of rocks with the right shape or configuration to hold the oil and gas and some kind of rock seal to prevent the oil and gas from leaving the reservoir. The reservoir rock is a container, and it usually holds a number of fluids in addition to the hydrocarbon (petroleum) deposit. For instance, the reservoir is almost always filled with a large amount of water as well as with the oil and gas. The fluids are usually layered with the gas on top, then the oil, and the water on the bottom—just like oil, water, and vinegar in a salad dressing bottle.

To qualify as a reservoir rock, a rock formation must be sufficiently large, porous, and thick to contain commercially profitable quantities of gas and oil. In practice, most commercial reservoir rocks are thicker than 10 feet and have porosities above 10 percent—that is, at least 10 percent of the rock is empty pore space, which could contain petroleum. Commercial reservoir rocks also must be permeable, which means that oil and gas (if present) must be able to move or flow from one pore space to another within the rock. The empty pore space in rocks can be filled with water alone; with water and oil; or with oil, gas, and water. Petroleum companies, of course, prefer that the rocks contain all three, because the oil and gas are profitable, and the water often assists in moving the oil and gas out of the rocks and into the well. Water and other substances force the petroleum to move by exerting pressure. Thus, commercial production ultimately depends upon the pressure, porosity, and permeability of the reservoir rock as much as on the rock's having a proper trap or a good seal to keep the petroleum in the reservoir. All of these factors are part of the petroleum geologist's concern in searching for a commercial petroleum deposit.

BASIC CONCEPTS OF GEOLOGY

Early history of the earth

The earth is thought to have originated some 4 to 5 billion years ago out of a condensing cloud of cosmic dust. Most theorists agree that at some time during its early life the earth must have passed through a molten or partially molten stage induced by gravitational compression or the release of energy by radioactive elements. During this molten phase, the components of the earth separated to produce a heavy core 4,400 miles in diameter, a mantle of lighter material some 1,800 miles thick, and a crust of the lightest materials some 10 to 30 miles thick (fig. 1.1). At the same time, large amounts of water vapor and gases erupted to form the primeval atmosphere. Slowly the crust cooled.

The earth shrank as it cooled, causing the crust to buckle and warp and a rugged surface to develop. At this time all the rocks were igneous in origin; that is, they had all solidified from a molten form called *magma*.

As the atmosphere developed and the earth cooled, rain began to fall. Water ran from the heights and collected in the low valleys and shallow depressions to form the primeval oceans. Erosion began when water removed particles of rock and carried them to lower places; sedimentation started when the particles settled out of the quiet water. Gradually, the face of the earth began to change.

Uplifted blocks of igneous rocks were worn down from their original form (shown by the broken line in fig. 1.2), and the valley between them partially filled with the resulting sediment. The configuration of an uplifted *horst* and down-dropped *graben* is a common surface feature, exemplified by the Red Sea between Asia and Africa.

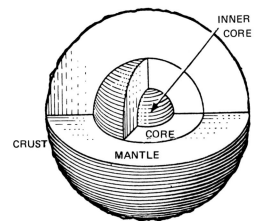

Figure 1.1. A cross section of the earth would show its crust, mantle, core, and inner core.

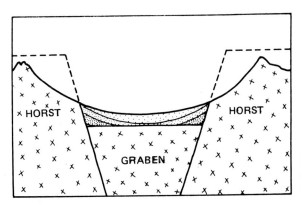

Figure 1.2. The uplifted horst and down-dropped graben are common surface features.

The earth was barren and lifeless for millions of years. Then at some indeterminate point in time, life began in the oceans. In fact, by the beginning of the Cambrian period, which was about 550 million years ago, life was abundant in the oceans (fig. 1.3). However, not until the Devonian period, about 350 million years ago, did vegetation become widespread on the land areas, and land animals became common even later (fig. 1.4).

Figure 1.3. Abundant sea life helped form petroleum pools on the ocean subfloor. *(Courtesy of Continental Oil Company and American Petroleum Institute)*

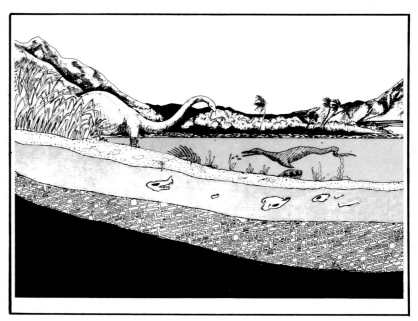

Figure 1.4. Plants and animals from prehistoric times form oil pools in land strata.

Because life has continuously evolved from Precambrian time, the fossil remains of animals and plants, called *fauna* and *flora,* succeed one another in a definite and determinable order. This has enabled the succession of rocks to be subdivided into eras and smaller subdivisions, the more important of which are shown in table 1.1.

Table 1.1
Geologic Time Scale

Era	Period	Epoch	Duration (millions of years)	Dates (millions of years)
Cenozoic	Quaternary	Recent	0.01	0.00
				0.01
		Pleistocene	1	
				1
	Tertiary	Pliocene	10	
				11
		Miocene	14	
				25
		Oligocene	15	
				40
		Eocene	20	
				60
		Paleocene	10	
				70 ± 2
Mesozoic	Cretaceous		65	
				135 ± 5
	Jurassic		30	
				165 ± 10
	Triassic		35	
				200 ± 20
Palezoic	Permian		35	
				235 ± 30
	Pennsylvanian		30	
				265 ± 35
	Mississippian		35	
				300 ± 40
	Devonian		50	
				350 ± 40
	Silurian		40	
				380 ± 40
	Ordovician		70	
				460 ± 40
	Cambrian		90	
				550 ± 50
Precambrian			4,500 ±	

(After R. M. Sneider)

The duration of the eras and subdivisions in years has been determined from studies of radioactive minerals. The presence of life is essential to the petroleum story because organic matter is one of the necessary ingredients in the formation of oil.

The rock cycle

Erosion is usually the result of flowing water, but it can result from the action of wind, freezing water, moving ice, and waves. The original particles that eroded from the surface of the earth were all derived from igneous rocks. Sediments continued to be deposited on sediments (fig. 1.5). The earlier unconsolidated deposits (*A*) were compacted by the weight of the overlying sediments (*B*) and in the process were transformed into sedimentary rocks. These in turn could be eroded again to produce sediments, and thus the cycle of erosion and sedimentation continued (fig. 1.6). Further, some sedimentary rocks were put under tremendous heat and pressure so that they were transformed into metamorphic rocks.

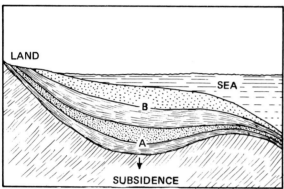

Figure 1.5. The weight of overlying unconsolidated sediments (*B*) compacts sediment layer (*A*) into sedimentary rocks.

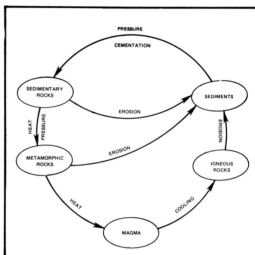

Figure 1.6. The rock cycle

Sedimentary rocks are important to petroleum geology since most oil and gas accumulations occur in them. (Igneous and metamorphic rocks rarely contain oil or gas.) Sedimentary rocks are deposited by water, wind, or ice. In general, older sedimentary rocks have been compacted by the weight of the overlying sediments or cemented by minerals carried by ground water, so that they become consolidated rock. Ground water is the water present in rock pores and cracks. A simple classification of sedimentary rocks is shown in table 1.2.

Table 1.2
Classification of Sedimentary Rocks

Clastic	Chemical		Organic	Other
	Carbonate	Evaporite		
Conglomerate Sandstone Siltstone Shale	Limestone Dolomite	Gypsum Anhydrite Salt Potash	Peat Coal Diatomite Limestone	Chert

If some other process did not compensate for erosion, the land would be reduced to plains near the level of the sea. However, the land currently stands about as high above sea level as it ever did. Obviously, uplift of the surface must have occurred to compensate for the wearing down of the mountains.

The surface of the earth and upper crust have moved upward, downward, or horizontally many times since the earth was formed. In fact, movements are continuing today, as the earthquakes that occur each year demonstrate. Sometimes only a few feet of displacement can be seen along a break, or fault, after an earthquake. However, remains of marine shells have been found in some of the highest mountains and in the deepest oil wells, proving that the rocks were deposited in some ancient sea and then uplifted or dropped to their present position. Geological evidence shows that repeated movements of only a few inches at a time will gradually raise or lower the earth's surface enough to account for total displacements of thousands of feet.

Sedimentary rocks are deposited in essentially horizontal layers called *strata*, or *beds*. Most rock layers are not strong enough to withstand the forces to which they are subjected and so become deformed. A common kind of deformation is the buckling of the layers into folds (fig. 1.7). Folds are the most common structures in mountain chains, ranging in size from small wrinkles to great arches and troughs many miles across. The upfolds or arches are called *anticlines;* the downfolds or troughs are *synclines* (fig. 1.8). A symmetrical fold with similar flanks dipping on both limbs is possible, as is an asymmetrical shape with one limb steeper than the other.

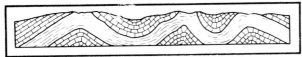

Figure 1.7. Schematic cross section shows deformation of earth's crust by buckling of layers into folds.

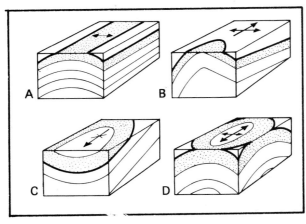

Figure 1.8. Simple kinds of folds are symmetrical anticline (*A*), plunging asymmetrical anticline (*B*), plunging syncline (*C*), and dome with deep salt core (*D*).

Anticlines and synclines both plunge. A short anticline with its crest plunging in opposite directions from a high point is called a *dome.* Domes often have an intrusive core that uplifts them, such as the salt domes along the U.S. Gulf Coast. Anticlines and domes are important to petroleum geologists because they often contain hydrocarbon deposits.

Earth movements

Most rocks are fractured during earth movement, resulting in cracks called *joints.* If the rock layers on one side of a fracture have moved in relation to the other side, the fracture is called a *fault* (fig. 1.9). Displacement—or how far apart the sides of the fault have moved—may range from only a few inches to many miles, as along the San Andreas fault in California.

A simple classification system outlines four kinds of faults: *normal, reverse, thrust,* and *lateral* (fig. 1.10). The names are derived from the movement of adjacent blocks. Movement is up or down in normal and reverse faults but is mainly horizontal in thrust and lateral faults. A combination of vertical and horizontal movements is also possible in all faults.

Rotational faults and upthrusts (fig. 1.11) are variations of normal and reverse faulting. They are most important to the petroleum geologist because they affect the location of oil and gas accumulations.

Earth movements often bury or prevent the depositing of part of a sediment series that is present elsewhere. Such buried erosion surfaces are called *unconformities.* Two general kinds of unconformities are the disconformity and the angular unconformity (fig. 1.12). Earth movements are most important to petroleum geology because they produce barriers that cause a large proportion of petroleum accumulations.

PETROLEUM ACCUMULATIONS

A petroleum accumulation must have (1) a source of oil and gas, (2) a porous and permeable bed or reservoir rock, and (3) a trap that acts as a barrier to fluid flow so that accumulation can occur.

Origin of petroleum

Oil and gas probably originated from organic matter in sedimentary rocks. The origin of coal on land is a process similar to the origin of petroleum in the sea. In the formation of coal, dead vegetation in the absence of oxygen ceases to decompose and accumulates as humus in the soil and as deposits of peat in bogs and swamps. Peat buried beneath a cover of clays and sands becomes compacted. As the weight and pressure of the cover increase, water and gases are driven off. The residue, very rich in carbon, becomes coal.

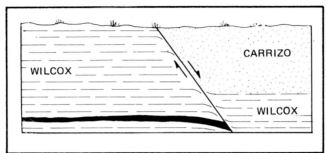

Figure 1.9. Simplified diagram of the Milano, Texas, fault

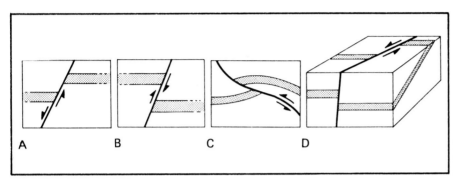

Figure 1.10. Simple kinds of faults are normal (*A*), reverse (*B*), thrust (*C*), and lateral (*D*).

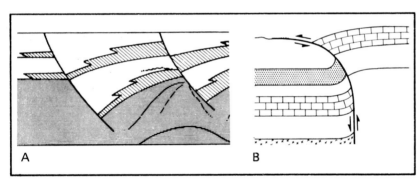

Figure 1.11. Variations of normal and reverse faulting are rotational faults (*A*) and upthrust faults (*B*).

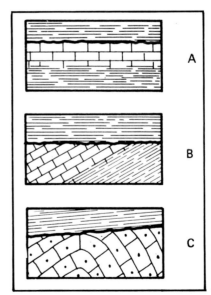

Figure 1.12. Two general kinds of unconformities are disconformity (*A*) and angular unconformities (*B* and *C*).

In the sea a similar process takes place. An abundance of marine life is eternally falling in a slow, steady rain to the bottom of the sea. Vast quantities of matter are eaten or oxidized before they reach the bottom, but a portion of this microscopic animal and plant residue escapes destruction and is entombed in the ooze and mud on the seafloor. The organic debris collects in sunken areas at the bottom and is buried within an ever-increasing accumulation of sands, clays, and more debris until the sediment is thousands of feet thick. As the sediment builds, the pressure of deep burial begins to work. Bacteria take oxygen from the trapped organic residues and gradually break down the matter, molecule by molecule, into substances rich in carbon and hydrogen. The extreme weight and pressure of the mass compacts and squeezes the clays into hard shales. Within this deep, unwitnessed realm of immense force, oil is born.

The generation of hydrocarbons from the source material depends primarily on the maximum temperature to which the organic material is subjected. Hydrocarbon generation appears to be negligible at temperatures less than about 150° F in the subsurface and reaches a maximum within the range of 225° F to 350° F. Increasing temperatures convert the heavy hydrocarbons to lighter ones and ultimately to gas. However, at temperatures above 500° F, the organic material is carbonized and destroyed as a source material. Consequently, it appears that source beds too deeply buried by earth movements produce no hydrocarbons because of the high temperatures at extreme depths.

After generation, the dispersed hydrocarbons in the fine-grained source rocks must be concentrated by migration to a reservoir. Compaction of the source beds by the weight of the overlying rocks expels the hydrocarbons from the source beds. The hydrocarbons then move out through more porous beds or through fractures to regions of lower pressure, which generally means to a shallower depth. Petroleum is, consequently, forever trying to rise until it is trapped or escapes at the surface of the earth.

Reservoir rocks

A *petroleum reservoir* is a rock capable of containing gas, oil, or water. To be commercially productive, it must be big enough, be thick enough, and have enough pore space to contain an appreciable volume of hydrocarbons. Also, it must give up the contained fluids at a satisfactory rate when the reservoir is penetrated by a well. Sandstones and carbonates (such as limestone and dolomite) are the most common reservoir rocks.

Close examination of a rock with a powerful magnifying glass reveals that there are openings in the rock, or pores. A rock with pores is said to be porous or to have *porosity*. The porosity of a formation controls its capacity for reservoir fluids. The greater a rock's porosity, the more fluids it is able to hold. Porosity may vary from less than 5 percent in a tightly cemented sandstone or carbonate to more than 30 percent for unconsolidated sands. Accurate determination of formation porosity is extremely difficult.

Besides porosity, a reservoir rock must also have *permeability;* that is, the pores of the rock must be connected. These connected pores allow petroleum to move from one pore to another; thus, when a well is drilled into a reservoir, the petroleum has a way to move out of the pores and into the well. The rock's permeability determines how easy or hard it is for the petroleum to move or flow within the rock.

The unit of measurement of permeability is the darcy. Most petroleum reservoirs have permeabilities so small that they are measured in thousandths of a darcy or millidarcies (md). The relationship between the porosity and the permeability of a given formation is not necessarily a close or direct one. However, high porosity is often accompanied by high permeability.

To sum up, if there is sufficient permeability and porosity in the reservoir rocks, then migration will occur, and it will be possible to have hydrocarbon accumulation. But, in order for this process to occur, there must first be a way of stopping migration.

Migration is a continuing process once the hydrocarbons have been generated and expelled from the source rock. Hydrocarbons will move ever upward until they escape at the surface unless something stops the movement. Therefore, a barrier, or trap, is needed to impede this migration in order to get a subsurface accumulation of petroleum.

Traps

A trap is produced by geological conditions that cause oil and gas to be retained in a porous reservoir. Reservoir traps for hydrocarbons have two general forms: (1) an arched upper surface, commonly called *structural,* and (2) an up-dip termination of porosity, called *stratigraphic* (fig. 1.13).

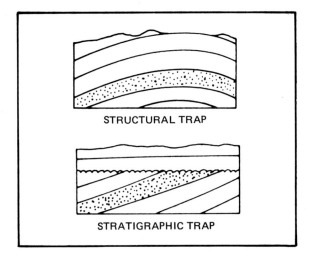

Figure 1.13. Basic hydrocarbon reservoirs are structural and/or stratigraphic traps.

Structural traps

A structural trap is formed by the folding or faulting of the rock layer that contains the hydrocarbons (fig. 1.14). Structural traps vary widely in size and shape. Some of the more common structural traps are anticlinal traps, fault traps, and dome and plug traps.

Reservoirs formed by the folding of rock layers, or strata, usually have the shape of structural domes or anticlines (fig. 1.15). These *anticlinal traps* were filled with petroleum when it moved in from its source below. In the anticline, further movement of petroleum was

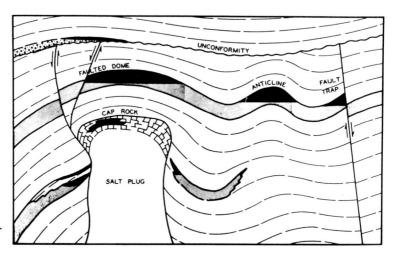

Figure 1.14. Common types of structural traps

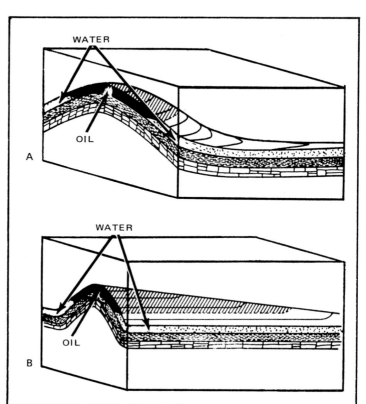

Figure 1.15. Oil accumulates in a dome-shaped structure (*A*) and an anticlinal type of fold structure (*B*). An anticline is generally long and narrow while the dome is circular in outline. *(Courtesy of American Petroleum Institute)*

arrested by the shape of the structure and by a seal or cap rock. Two examples of oil fields that have anticlinal traps are the Santa Fe Springs field in California and the Agha Jari field in Iran.

Fault traps are formed by breaking or shearing and offsetting of strata (fig. 1.16). The escape of oil from such a trap is prevented by nonporous rocks that have moved into a position opposite the porous petroleum-bearing formation. The oil is confined in traps of this type because of the tilt of the rock layers and the faulting. A fault trap depends on the effectiveness of the seal at the fault. The seal may be formed by an impermeable bed that moved opposite the permeable reservoir bed. For example, shale is impermeable and can thus form a seal. Or a seal may be caused by impermeable material called *gouge* within the fault zone itself. The simple fault trap may occur where structural contours provide closure against a single fault. However, in other structural configurations, two or even three faults may be required to form a trap (fig. 1.17). Fault trap accumulations tend to be elongated and parallel to the fault trend; for example, the accumulations in the numerous oil fields along the Mexia-Talco fault zone extend from central to northeastern Texas.

Dome and plug traps are porous formations on or surrounding great plugs or masses of salt or serpentine rock that have pierced,

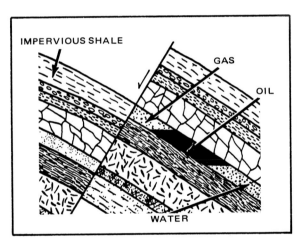

Figure 1.16. Gas and oil are trapped in a fault trap—a reservoir resulting from normal faulting or offsetting of strata. The block on the right has moved up from the block on the left, moving impervious shale opposite the hydrocarbon-bearing formation. *(Courtesy of American Petroleum Institute)*

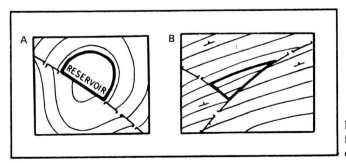

Figure 1.17. Shown in map view, fault traps may be simple (*A*) or compound (*B*).

deformed, or lifted the overlying rock layers (figs. 1.18 and 1.19). Piercement may be more or less circular, which is typical of the salt-dome oil fields in the U.S. Gulf Coast and Germany, or they can be long and narrow as in the oil fields of Romania. The salt and associated material form an efficient up-dip seal; that is, the hydrocarbons cannot migrate upward or out of the reservoir because it is sealed by the salt. Hydrocarbon accumulations in the peripheral traps around a salt plug may not be continuous. Instead, oil accumulations are usually broken into several separate segments. As a result, many smaller traps are formed by many smaller faults or are closed off against the plug (fig. 1.20). This discontinuous nature of oil accumulations in piercement traps makes it very difficult to drill successfully. The geologist knows that the traps are there; he just cannot accurately predict their precise location. As a result, many dry holes are drilled in attempts to tap the reservoir.

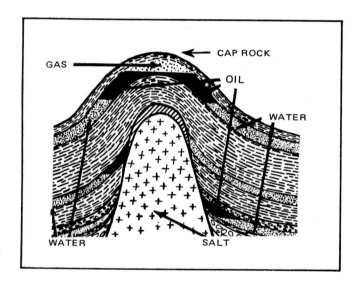

Figure 1.18. A nonporous salt mass has formed dome-shaped traps in overlying and surrounding porous rocks. *(Courtesy of American Petroleum Institute)*

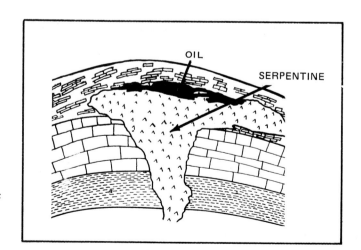

Figure 1.19. A porous serpentine plug forms a reservoir within itself by intruding into nonporous surrounding formations. *(Courtesy of American Petroleum Institute)*

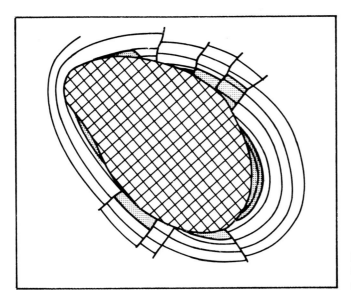

Figure 1.20. Discontinuous peripheral traps form around a piercement salt dome.

Stratigraphic traps

A stratigraphic trap is caused either by a nonporous formation sealing off the top edge of a reservoir bed or by a change of porosity and permeability within the reservoir bed itself (fig. 1.21). Two general kinds of stratigraphic traps are the *disconformity* and the *angular unconformity,* both resulting from unconformities. Often part of the depositional sequence was eroded, thereby putting porous and permeable oil-bearing rock in contact with an impermeable cap rock. In a disconformity, the beds above and below the surface of unconformity are parallel. In an angular unconformity, the beds above the unconformity are spread across the eroded edges of folded and tilted beds below. This type of reservoir can be formed when the upward movement of oil is halted by an impermeable cap rock laid down across the cutoff surfaces of the lower beds (fig. 1.22). An example of this type of reservoir is the East Texas field.

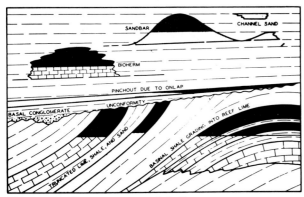

Figure 1.21. Common types of stratigraphic traps

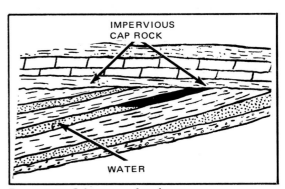

Figure 1.22. Oil is trapped under an unconformity. *(Courtesy of API)*

A *lenticular trap* is one that is sealed in its upper regions by abrupt changes in the amount of connected pore space within a formation. This may be caused, in the case of sandstones, by irregular depositing of sand and shale at the time the formation was laid down. In these cases, oil is confined within porous parts of the rock by the nonporous parts of the rock surrounding it (fig. 1.23). Lenticular traps pinch out or change permeability on all sides and are fairly common in carbonate rocks. They occur usually in the upper part of carbonate buildups, commonly called reefs, which may contain very large petroleum accumulations. However, reefs are rarely filled by hydrocarbons, so the lower parts of the reservoir contain water.

Combination traps

Another common type of reservoir is formed by a combination of folding, faulting, changes in porosity, and other conditions—some structural and some stratigraphic in origin. Examples of reservoirs of this nature are the many reservoirs found in the Seeligson field in Southwest Texas or parts of the East Texas field.

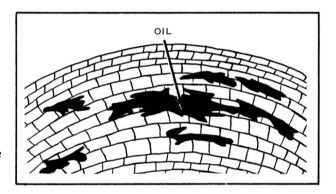

Figure 1.23. Lenticular traps confine oil in porous parts of the rock. *(Courtesy of API)*

RESERVOIR FLUIDS AND PRESSURE

Types of reservoir fluids

By definition, a fluid is any substance that will flow. Oil, water, and gas are all fluids; oil and water are liquids as well as fluids; gas is a fluid but not a liquid.

Water

Oil reservoirs are composed of sediments that were deposited on the seafloor (fig. 1.24). Consequently, these sedimentary beds were originally saturated with salt water. However, part of this water was displaced by petroleum when it was formed. Salt water that remains in the formation is called connate interstitial water—*connate* from the Latin meaning "born with" and *interstitial* because the water is found in the interstices, or pores, of the formation. By common usage this term has been shortened to *connate water* and always means the water

Figure 1.24. Sedimentary beds on the seafloor were originally saturated with salt water, which was partially displaced by petroleum when it was formed.

in the formation when development of the reservoir was started.

Invariably some connate water is distributed throughout the reservoir. Besides connate water, nearly all petroleum reservoirs have additional water that accumulated along with the petroleum. It is this "free" water that supplies the energy for the water drive in some reservoirs. *Bottom water* occurs beneath the oil accumulation; *edgewater* occurs at the edge of the oil zone on the flanks of the structure.

Oil

Oil, which is lighter than water and will not mix with it, makes room for itself in the void space of the reservoir rock by pushing the water downward. However, oil will not displace all the original water. A film of water sticks to, or is adsorbed by, the solid rock material surrounding the pore spaces. The film of water lining the pores is called *wetting water*. In other words, water is not only in the reservoir below the oil accumulation, but also within the pores along with the oil.

Gas

Natural gas is always associated with oil produced from a reservoir. The energy supplied by gas under pressure is probably the most valuable drive in the withdrawal of oil from reservoirs. The industry has come a long way since the day it was general practice to "blow" gas caps into the atmosphere, so that a well in the gas zone of a reservoir could finally be induced to produce a little crude oil. Gas is associated with oil and water in reservoirs in two principal ways, as *solution gas* and as *free gas* in gas caps.

Given proper conditions of pressure and temperature, natural gas will stay in solution in oil in a reservoir. High pressure and low temperature are favorable conditions for keeping gas in solution. When the oil is brought to the surface and the pressure relieved, the gas comes out of solution, much as a bottle of soda water fizzes when the cap is removed. Gas in solution occupies space in a reservoir, and allowance has to be made for this space when calculating the volume of oil in place.

Free gas—gas that is not dissolved in oil—tends to accumulate in the highest structural part of a reservoir where it forms a gas cap. As long as there is free gas in a reservoir gas cap, the oil in the reservoir will remain saturated with gas in solution. Having gas in solution lowers the resistance of oil to flow, or the viscosity of the oil, thereby making the oil easier to move to the wellbore.

Fluid distribution

The oil-water contact line (the point in the reservoir where the oil and water touch) is of prime interest to all concerned in the early development of a field, because to get maximum production from the reservoir, the water should not be produced with the oil. Practically all reservoirs have water in the lowest portions of the formation, and the oil lies just above it. However, no sharp line divides the oil and water, nor is the contact line horizontal throughout a reservoir. Actually, the oil-water contact is a zone of part water and part oil, and this zone may be from 10 to 15 feet thick. The gas-oil contact has somewhat the same properties. However, because oil is much heavier than gas, oil does not tend to rise as high into the gas zone as water does into the oil zone.

Reservoir pressure

Every reservoir that contains fluids contains those fluids under pressure. Pressure exists in a reservoir for the same reason that pressure exists at the bottom of the ocean. Consider a person who is swimming in a large swimming pool or lake. As he swims along the surface, he suddenly decides to see if he can touch bottom. So under he goes, bravely kicking his way to the bottom. Everything is going well except that his ears begin to hurt, and the closer he gets to the bottom—the deeper he dives, the more his ears hurt. The reason for the pain is that the pressure of the water is pressing against his eardrum. The deeper he goes, the greater the pressure and the more his ears hurt.

Normal pressure

Just as there is water pressure in a swimming pool, there is water pressure in a reservoir. Under normal conditions, the only pressure that exists in a reservoir is the pressure caused by the water in it. Contrary to what might seem logical, all the rocks that overlie a buried reservoir do not create pressure in the reservoir under normal circumstances. Instead, it is as if there are no rocks there at all—at least as far as pressure is concerned.

To return to the swimming pool analogy, imagine leaving the pool full of water but dumping a huge load of marbles into it. Naturally, the marbles would take up volume formerly taken up by water, and the pool would overflow; water would slosh over the sides. However, a pressure measurement taken at the bottom of the pool *before* the marbles were dumped in would be exactly the same *after* the marbles are put in. The pressure exerted by the water remains the same.

The same thing happens in a reservoir. Of course, in a reservoir the "marbles" do not often reach the surface. Instead, the reservoir connection to the surface is usually much more circuitous; it could outcrop on the surface many miles from the point where it lies buried, or it could be connected to the surface through other porous beds that overlie it. In any case, as long as the reservoir has some ultimate outlet to the surface, the pressure in it is caused only by the water and is considered to be normal pressure.

Reservoirs that do not have a connection with the surface are totally surrounded by impermeable formations. In such cases, the overlying rock formations do have a bearing on reservoir pressure. What happens in this case is that the heavy weight of the overlying beds presses down and squeezes the reservoir. Since the water in the reservoir cannot escape to the surface, the reservoir pressure builds up to abnormally high amounts. It is somewhat like blowing up a balloon, tying it off so the air cannot escape, and then squeezing it. Since the air in it is confined, the pressure builds and builds until the balloon pops. Reservoirs do not pop, but the pressure builds.

Abnormal pressure

Another way in which abnormally high pressure can exist is when there is an artesian effect (fig. 1.25). In this case, the reservoir does connect with the surface. However, the outcrop to the surface is on the side of a hill or mountain, at an elevation much higher than the part of the reservoir buried below the level plain. A well drilled at this point spouts water like a fountain. The water tries to seek its own level. Such wells are called artesian wells.

RESERVOIR DRIVES

Oil, gas, and water in a reservoir are of no value unless they can be moved from their location to a well and then to the surface. Several types of energy drives are used to move petroleum out of the reservoirs. Reservoir rocks occur in layers, usually as a permeable formation between impermeable layers, and this structure is the dominant feature of the drive mechanisms.

Depletion drive operates when the reservoir is "closed"; that is, no large amounts of water contact the hydrocarbons in the reservoir. The expansion of the hydrocarbons in the reservoir provides the only energy for the oil or gas to reach the wellbore and move toward the surface. Two kinds of depletion drives are solution-gas drive and gas-cap drive.

Depletion drive

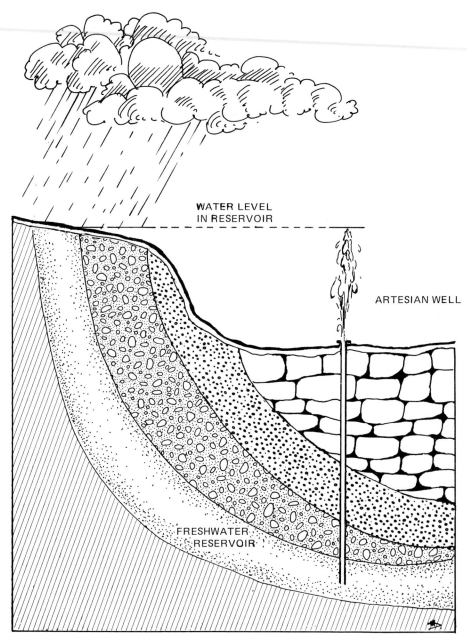

Figure 1.25. Abnormally high formation pressure can be artesian in nature.

Solution-gas drive

In a solution-gas drive reservoir (known also as dissolved-gas drive), the lighter hydrocarbon components that exist as a liquid in the reservoir before it is produced come out in the form of gas as the reservoir is produced. The solution gas coming out of the oil expands to force the oil into the wellbore (fig. 1.26). In solution-gas drive reservoirs, pressure declines rapidly and continuously, and wells generally require pumping or some other artificial lift at an early stage. The gas-oil ratio (the amount of gas compared to the amount of oil being produced) is low initially, then rises to a maximum and drops. With the exception of possible edge wells, which may have penetrated the oil-water contact, there is little or no water production. Recovery efficiency (how much oil is ultimately produced) varies from as little as 5 percent to as much as 30 percent of the original oil in place.

A gas-cap drive is a depletion drive in a reservoir that has a gas cap. As pressure is reduced in the oil zone by withdrawal, the gas cap expands and pushes oil out ahead of it (fig. 1.27). Performance in this type reservoir is similar to solution-gas drive, but pressure declines may be slower because the gas cap provides a lot of drive energy. Gas-oil ratios rise continuously in upstructure wells with this type drive, with little or no water production existing except in those wells that penetrate the reservoir near its edge. Due to the presence of more energy in the whole system, there may be a long-flowing life, depending on the size of the gas cap, and oil recovery may be from 20 to 40 percent of the original oil in place.

Gas-cap drive

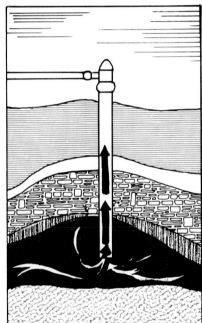

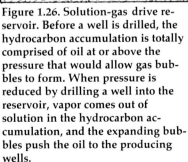

Figure 1.26. Solution-gas drive reservoir. Before a well is drilled, the hydrocarbon accumulation is totally comprised of oil at or above the pressure that would allow gas bubbles to form. When pressure is reduced by drilling a well into the reservoir, vapor comes out of solution in the hydrocarbon accumulation, and the expanding bubbles push the oil to the producing wells.

Figure 1.27. Gas-cap drive. Arrows depict the idea that as pressure is reduced in the oil zone by withdrawal, the gas cap expands and pushes oil out ahead of it.

22

Water drive

Water drive occurs when there is enough energy available from water in the reservoir to move the hydrocarbons out of the reservoir, into the wellbore, and up to the surface (fig. 1.28). The water in most water-bearing formations develops fluid pressure equivalent to the depth beneath the surface; in other words, the deeper the water, the higher the pressure.

Water is quite efficient at displacing oil from reservoir rock, and only a small amount of residual oil is left behind. As the oil is driven out of the reservoir, the water moves in to replace it. This is about the same as emptying a tank of oil by displacing the oil in the tank with water injected at the bottom. Thus, the pressure remains high as long as the volume of oil withdrawn is replaced by an approximately equivalent volume of water. If the reservoir pressure remains high, the surface gas-oil ratio remains low because little or no free gas is evolved in the reservoir. Because a high reservoir pressure is maintained, wells usually flow on their own until water production becomes excessive and kills the well. Water production may start early and increase to an appreciable amount as water encroaches into the oil and into the producing wells. Expected oil recovery with water drive is generally higher—up to 50 percent or more of the oil originally in place—because of the greater displacement efficiency of water over gas.

Water-drive reservoirs can have bottom-water drive or edgewater drive.

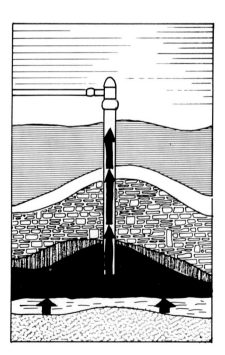

Figure 1.28. Water drive reservoir. The oil is associated with the water-bearing formation. Arrows indicate the encroachment of water, which drives oil toward and out of the producing well.

In a bottom-water drive reservoir, the oil accumulation is totally underlain by water. A well drilled anywhere through this reservoir penetrates oil first and then water.

Bottom-water drive

In an edgewater drive reservoir, the oil accumulation almost completely fills the reservoir. Water occurs only on the edges of the reservoir, thus only wells drilled along the edges penetrate water. Wells drilled near the top of the structure penetrate oil only.

Edgewater drive

Depletion and water drives can be characterized as pure types of drive mechanisms. However, many reservoirs have a combination drive. One such drive has a gas cap above the oil and water below it. Both the gas cap and the water serve to drive oil into and up the well to the surface. Another type of combination drive has gas dissolved in the oil and water below it. Gas coming out of solution and the water both operate to drive oil to the surface.

Combination drive

A less common type of drive mechanism is gravity drainage. The force of gravity is always at work in a reservoir. Oil, as all other liquids, runs downhill under the influence of gravity. If the hill is steep enough, a well may be produced by permitting the oil to flow almost exclusively under the influence of gravitational forces.

Gravity drainage

Gravity drainage is often the dominant drive mechanism in shallow, highly permeable, steeply dipping reservoirs and may occur in deeper reservoirs late in the depletion life. While gas or water drive is certainly a stronger force than gravity, gravity is at least a force in the right direction.

RESERVOIR MAINTENANCE

Restricted production of oil from reservoirs with good water drives and large gas caps generally yields a greater return of both oil and profit than can be obtained if haphazard and inefficient production methods are employed. If weak water or gas-cap drives are caused by lower reservoir permeability, the reservoir pressure may be maintained fairly high by reducing the production rate or by carefully controlling the amount of free gas or water being produced. If control cannot be accomplished, supplementing the inadequate natural drives by pressure maintenance operations and the use of secondary recovery methods will usually lead to greater oil recovery.

Pressure maintenance

Pressure maintenance is improving inadequate natural drives by injecting gas or water into the reservoir before the pressure drops appreciably, thus maintaining oil displacement energy at a high level. Gas or water may be injected into the reservoir through wells that are specially drilled for that purpose, or gas or water may be injected through already existing wells that are modified for injection purposes. With natural gas in short supply and getting scarcer, most pressure maintenance is done today with water injection.

The chief objectives of pressure maintenance operations are to force gas or water through the oil zone of the reservoir and physically to displace oil out of the pore spaces and into the wellbores. This procedure can assist displacement drives already present and replace natural dissolved-gas drives. Pressure maintenance can also assist the displacement process by keeping the oil in a gas-saturated state, which keeps the viscosity low so that the oil moves more easily. In addition, maintaining high pressure aids oil flow to the wells.

Secondary recovery

Primary recovery is oil recovery during a well's initial phase of development that utilizes naturally occurring reservoir forces or the conventional mechanical and physical pumping methods. For many reasons, a reservoir may approach the end of its primary life having produced only a small fraction of the oil in place. Production of the reservoir may have been started before good development and production practices were known. Unknown problems such as a casing leak or blowout could result in wasted reservoir energy, or the owner might not be willing to invest more money for maintenance while wells are producing profitably. However, even with the best primary production methods, a great deal of oil is left behind. Secondary recovery is defined as an operation wherein a depleted or nearly depleted reservoir is rejuvenated.

The most common secondary recovery method is waterflooding, in which water is injected into the depleted reservoir. It is most effective in depletion drive reservoirs in which little or no water drive was ever in force. In such reservoirs, waterflooding becomes, in effect, a man-made water drive: the water forces the oil, which was left behind by the depletion drive, out of the reservoir.

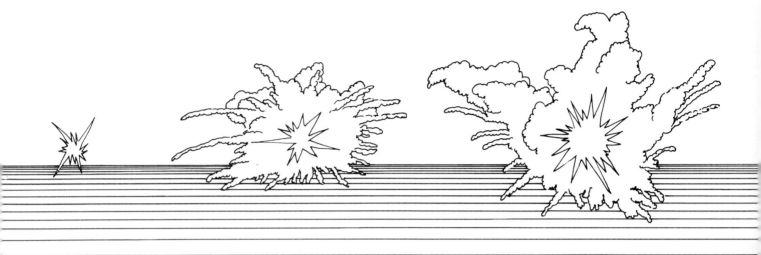

Petroleum Prospecting

P rospecting for petroleum was once a matter of good luck and guesswork; now it is based on many technical and scientific principles. The most successful oil-finding method in the early days of oil exploration was to drill in the vicinity of oil seeps, places where oil was actually present on the surface. Today, oil and gas discoveries are generally credited to subsurface geology studies. Data gathered with various geophysical instruments, cuttings made by the bit as the well is drilled, core samples taken from the well, and special graphs called logs that are generated by running special tools into the well as it is drilled—all yield important subsurface information. This information is used to prepare many kinds of maps and cross sections—maps that show the depth and shape of subsurface structures or variations in the characteristics of the rocks. Examining, correlating, and interpreting all the data make it possible for the petroleum industry to accurately locate subsurface structures that could contain hydrocarbon accumulations.

Many of the great oil fields of the world were discovered, in part at least, because of the presence of oil seeps. Oil seeps are located either up-dip or along fractures (fig. 2.1). Seeps at the outcrop of a reservoir bed may be active where oil or gas is still flowing out slowly, as at Mene Grande, Venezuela, only a mile up-dip from a large oil field. In other cases, the sands near the surface are completely sealed, and the seep is no longer active, as at Coalinga Field, California. The Athabaska "tar" sands in Canada appear to be a similar seep of the Cretaceous age. These sands were buried by later sediments and then exposed again by erosion. Seepage from fractures and faults is common and may be oil, gas, or mud (i.e., the mud volcanoes of Trinidad and Russia).

The presence of oil seeps on anticlinal crests was observed as early as 1842. However, not until after the drilling of the famous Drake well in Pennsylvania in 1859 was it noted that newly discovered wells were being located on anticlines. Little practical use was made of this information until 1885 when I. C. White applied it in search of gas in Pennsylvania and nearby states. During the latter part of the nineteenth century, geologists searched for oil in the East Indies and Mexico. In 1897, geological departments were established by some U.S. oil companies. Many of the subsequent discoveries in the Midcontinent, Gulf Coast, California, and elsewhere were made with the application of geology to the problem of finding petroleum reservoirs.

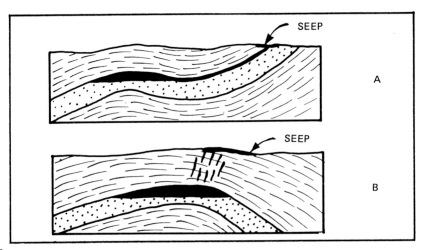

Figure 2.1. Seeps are located either up-dip (*A*) or along fractures (*B*).

EXPLORATION GEOPHYSICS

By 1920, anticlinal folding was only one of the geological factors known to control oil and gas accumulations. Surface mapping alone left much to be desired. Fortunately, geophysical methods of exploration came into existence about this time.

Geophysics deals with the composition and physical phenomena of the earth and its liquid and gaseous environments. The phenomena most commonly interpreted in petroleum exploration are earth magnetism, gravity, and especially seismic vibrations. Sensitive instruments are used to measure variations in a physical quality that may be related to subsurface conditions. These conditions, in turn, point to probable oil- or gas-bearing formations. Prospecting via geophysical means does not guarantee a successful find for each survey any more than other methods, but the combination of geophysical information and geological know-how reduces the chances of drilling a dry hole (fig. 2.2).

Geophysical prospecting depends on a few fundamental variables in the earth's physical condition: gravitational change, magnetic field change, time change, and electrical resistance change in the earth. The ideas used by geophysicists to develop explorational models for petroleum prospecting were taken from mineral studies.

Figure 2.2. Seismic exploration leads geophysicists from the deserts of Saudi Arabia (*A*) to Utah's canyon lands (*B*) and into the freezing plains of Alaska (*C*). *(Courtesy of API)*

Figure 2.3. A surveyor helps determine site location for seismic operations. *(Courtesy of API)*

The tools used by early geophysicists were fairly basic (fig. 2.3). The first geophysical instruments used for oil and gas exploration were the surface magnetometer, the refraction seismograph, and the torsion balance for gravimetric surveying. These were followed by reflection seismographs, gravimeters, and airborne magnetometers.

The most recent inventions enable geophysicists to explore, not only the surface and subsurface conditions of the earth for petroleum, but the lunar surface and depths as well. From this information, geologists and geophysicists gain valuable insights into the original processes that formed the earth, the moon, and the planets, which they can use to improve methods of geophysical prospecting.

Seismic method

The first seismograph, or seismometer as inventor David Milne called it, was used in 1841 to measure and record the vibrations of the ground during earthquakes. A few years later, Italian L. Palmieri set up a similar instrument, which he called a seismograph, on Mount Vesuvius. From these simple beginnings evolved seismic exploration.

Dr. L. Mintrop, a German scientist, developed one of the first practical uses of seismic data during World War I. He invented a portable seismograph (fig. 2.4) for the German armies to use in locating the positions of the Allied guns. Mintrop set up three seismographs on the battlefield opposite Allied artillery, and, when a gun fired, he calculated the precise location so accurately that often the Germans could wipe out that position with one try.

The Germans perceived that miscalculations in distance were due to the variation of sound waves caused by the geological formations through which the waves passed. Basic geological concepts were then applied, resulting in correct computations of the distance (fig. 2.5).

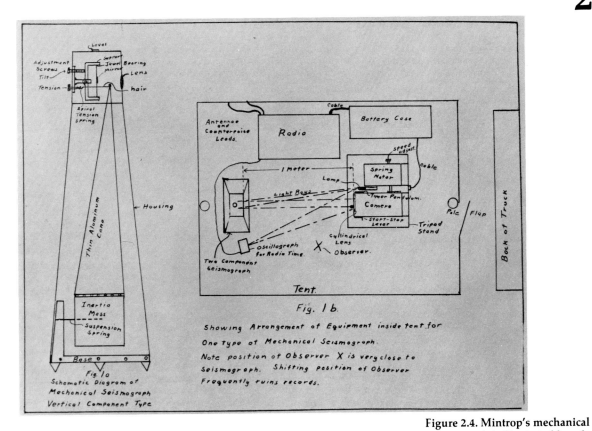

Figure 2.4. Mintrop's mechanical seismograph is illustrated here by Marck C. Malamphy and appeared in "Factors in Design of Portable Field Seismographs," *The Oil Weekly*, March 22, 1929. *(Courtesy of O. Scott Petty)*

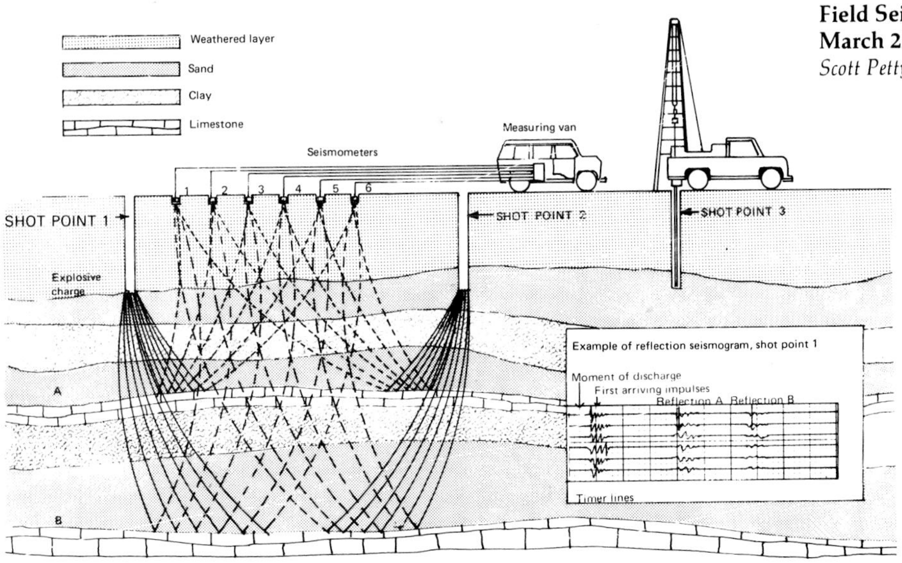

Figure 2.5. In seismic surveying, an explosion at shot point 1 creates shock waves that are reflected by subsurface formations to seismometers and are recorded on the truck.

After the war, Mintrop reversed the process to measure the distance from the explosion to the seismograph and thus estimate the geological subsurface formations. Finding his theories to be corroborated in the field, he put them into practice, forming the first seismic exploration company, Seismos. Soon after the company was started, the Gulf Production Company hired one of the Seismos crews and brought them to the Gulf Coast of Texas. With their arrival, news of seismic exploration spread, and soon rival companies were opening all over the state.

Two enterprising young brothers—Dabney E. and O. Scott Petty—decided to improve on Dr. Mintrop's methods. They resigned their jobs and spent a year developing a machine much more sensitive than Mintrop's. Their new seismograph used a vacuum tube sensitive enough to register the vibration of a "fly landing on a bar of steel," as O. Scott Petty explained it. The Petty Geophysical Engineering Company was established and became one of the early leaders in the field.

By the mid-1920s, the Pettys were "doodlebugging" (prospecting for oil) down by the Texas coast and in the Louisiana swamp (fig. 2.6). They hired an ingenious blacksmith named Pop Reichert to be their shot man—to set off the dynamite as the Pettys recorded the explosions on their instruments several miles away. He was a good mechanic and a fine fellow but had a bad habit of sitting on his dynamite (fig. 2.7). They warned him each morning that the dynamite was about 60 percent nitroglycerine, and he would be blown sky high if any of the flying debris from the blast fell on the box he was sitting on. One morning they decided to use a very large shot—300 pounds rather than their usual 5- to 30-pound charges—to get more accurate results. That morning they almost lost their shot man. As usual, he was sitting on a box of explosives too near the shot, and the secondary explosion of hydrogen and oxygen that sometimes follows a blast almost buried him under flying dirt. After that, he was careful to sit far enough away.

Most of the methods used by these early geophysical pioneers have been replaced or supplemented by newer reflection methods. Various mechanical impactors and vibrators have been developed to create sound waves on the earth's surface that penetrate downward into the rock layers. Each formation reflects the sound waves back to the surface where sensitive instruments record and measure the intensity of the reflections. By interpreting the measurements, geophysicists are able to locate formations likely to contain hydrocarbons.

One of the first nondynamite sources of surface energy was the *Thumper*, developed by Petty-Ray Geophysical (fig. 2.8). This impactor drops a heavy steel slab from as high as 9 feet to the surface, creating shock waves. Later, Sinclair Oil and Gas Company developed the *Dinoseis*, which uses a mixture of propane and oxygen

Figure 2.6. Doodlebugging in Chacahoula Swamp (note seismograph on stump). *(Courtesy of O. Scott Petty)*

Figure 2.7. Pop Reichert poses with his first, wooden shot-hole drilling rig. *(Courtesy of O. Scott Petty)*

Figure 2.8. This Thumper drops a 6,000-pound steel slab (surrounded by safety chains to warn personnel) 9 feet to strike earth and create shock waves. Weight-dropping aids the oil search as an effective economical substitute for dynamite in seismic operations.

Figure 2.9. The Vibroseis has a vibrator mounted underneath a truck that creates low-frequency sound waves. Geophones pick up the sonic reflections for recording.

in an expandable chamber to create an explosion. The explosion chamber is mounted under a truck and is lowered to the ground for use. Most commonly used today for land exploration is the *Vibroseis,* developed by Continental Oil Company (fig. 2.9). The Vibroseis generates continuous low-frequency sound waves whose reflections are picked up and changed into electrical impulses by instruments called geophones. These impulses are recorded on computer tape, processed on high-speed computers, and printed in the form of a seismic reflection profile. The profile is then interpreted to determine subsurface structures.

Marine seismic reflection methods consist primarily of the common depth point techniques and profiling. Widely used as energy sources for marine exploration are various models of an air gun, a device that discharges air under high pressure into the water, producing a bubble of high-pressure air. As the bubble oscillates, seismic waves are generated, recorded, and interpreted. Some of the models used are the *Unipulse, Vaporchoc, Flerotin, Aquapulse, Maxipulse,* and *Aquaseis.* Hydrophones—a marine version of geophones—are used for recording data.

Seismic experiments are not only conducted on land and sea, but also on the moon (fig. 2.10). The same principles of mathematics and science that are employed to explore the earth's subsurface led to the sophisticated technology used in the moon shots to explore the lunar subsurface. Just as Dr. Mintrop set up his three seismographs in a triangular arrangement in order to pinpoint the Allied guns, Apollo astronauts set up several seismic stations, each containing four

A

B

Figure 2.10. Seismic equipment on the lunar surface: *A*, deployed mortar assembly during active experiment; and *B*, seismometer after deployment during passive experiment. *(Courtesy of NASA)*

seismographs. The several experiments included an "active" one, which generated and monitored seismic waves in the near lunar surface, and a "passive" one, which monitored naturally occurring and man-made seismic disturbances on the lunar surface.

Methods of lunar seismic experimentation are similar to geophysical seismic methods. The astronauts carried a thumper, which could be activated by hand, and they set up a mortar package that contained rocket-launched grenades designed to be detonated later. In addition, the impact of the lunar module was monitored by the active seismic experiment.

Magnetic method

The fact that the earth has a strong magnetic field has been turned to good use by scientists engaged in the search for minerals. By applying the principle that some rocks are susceptible to magnetism and others are not, scientists can conduct magnetic surveys over an area and have a fairly clear idea of where the oil-bearing rocks are located. They can do this because they know that most oil occurs in sedimentary rocks, which are usually nonmagnetic. Igneous and metamorphic rock, which do not often contain oil, are highly magnetized. Thus, by conducting a magnetic survey of an area, a prospector has a general idea of where oil-bearing rocks are most likely to be found.

To measure the slight differences in magnetism in rocks, two delicate instruments are used: a *field balance* and an *airborne magnetometer.* A field balance is used on the earth's surface and measures the differences in magnetism rather than the true or absolute magnetic variation of an area. The airborne magnetometer measures and records the magnitude of the earth's total magnetic field that is associated principally with variations in the depth of burial of magnetized rocks. By calculation, geophysicists can ascertain the depth of basement rock and get a fairly good picture of the configuration of its geological formations. Geological anomalies associated with basement rock configurations can then be analyzed for possible oil- and gas-bearing formations.

Valuable insights into the magnetic processes of the earth have recently been gained from lunar magnetic experiments. Besides conducting seismic experiments, the astronauts also set up a lunar-surface magnetic observatory. A network of three sensors allows simultaneous measurements of the global response of the moon to large-scale solar and terrestrial magnetic fields (fig. 2.11). In addition to the permanent stations, astronauts also had a lunar portable magnetometer with which to measure the permanent magnetic field at different geological sites on the lunar surface (fig. 2.12). These measurements can be used to determine the present magnetic and structural properties of the local region and to explain magnetic aspects of the history of the moon.

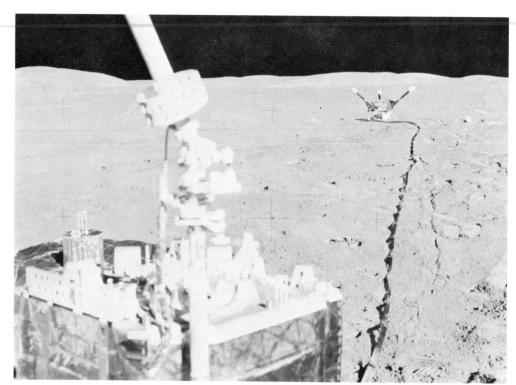

**Figure 2.11.Lunar-surface
magnetometer experiment**
(Courtesy of NASA)

**Figure 2.12.Lunar portable
magnetometer** *(Courtesy of NASA)*

Geophysical prospecting also makes use of what scientists know about the earth's gravitational field and the way it varies according to differences in mass distribution near the earth's surface. Simply explained, some rocks are denser than others; and, if very dense rocks are close to the surface, the gravitational force they exert is more powerful than that of a layer of very light rocks. The difference in mass for equal volumes of rock is due to variations in specific gravity. Geophysicists applied this knowledge, particularly in the early days of prospecting off the Gulf Coast; they could often locate salt domes by gravitational prospecting because the ordinary domal and anticlinal structures are associated with maximum gravity whereas salt domes are usually associated with minimum gravity.

The torsion balance, first marketed commercially in 1922, was one of the earliest gravitational instruments invented. It, as well as another early instrument, the pendulum, was rather difficult to use. The most commonly employed instrument is the gravimeter, a sensitive weighing instrument for measuring variations in the gravitational field of the earth. Technological advances enable geophysicists to use ever-improving equipment, but the basic principle of the gravitational method remains the same (fig. 2.13).

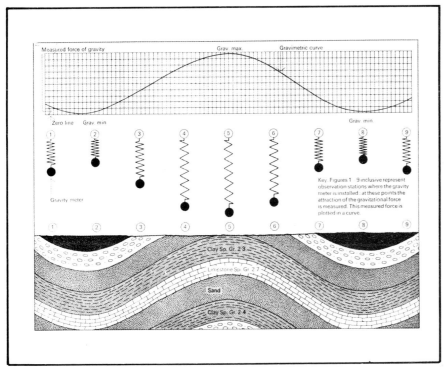

Figure 2.13. Principles of a gravity meter survey

38

STRATIGRAPHY: A PROSPECTING TOOL

Stratigraphic correlation

Stratigraphy is the study of the origin, composition, distribution, and succession of rock *strata*, which are distinct, generally parallel beds of rock. Stratigraphers try to recognize and follow beds of rock from one well to another, going from a well or formation whose beds and lithologic (rock) sequence is known to an area that is unknown but assumed to be similar. A stratigraphic test, or strat test as it is commonly called, involves drilling a well primarily to obtain geological information. The well exposes complete sections of the formations penetrated, and well samples are segments of the rock taken from the wellbore as it is drilled.

Stratigraphic correlation consists of matching strata, fossils, rock hardness or softness, and electrical data from one well to another or from one outcrop to another (fig. 2.14). Wells that have information collected by drillers' logs, sample logs, time logs, and electrical logs enable the geologists to predict more precisely where similar rock formations will occur in each case.

Subsurface correlation is based primarily on stratigraphic continuity, or the fact that formations maintain the same thickness

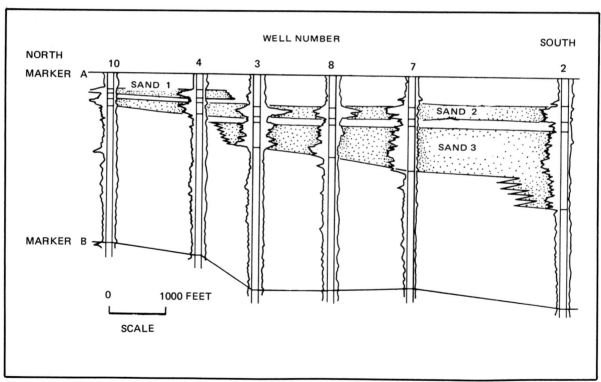

Figure 2.14. This stratigraphic cross section shows the effect of pinch-out of sand 3.

from one well to another. Any change in thickness can be a geologic indicator of a change in the conditions that formed the strata or may be a signal of an event that could cause petroleum to accumulate.

Correlation is also based on lithologic and faunal continuity. Formations, particularly marine ones, change rock texture and fossil characteristics only very gradually. Thus, sudden changes in lithologic sequence are geologic indicators, and often particular fossils are used as markers for geologists trying to recognize the continuation of a formation in a new location. If the kind of rock is the same, and if the fossil markers are the same, it is probably a continuation of the same formation.

The sequence of beds can also be used as a method of correlation. This method depends, as do the others in part, on drilling closely spaced wells so that the beds can be matched accurately as the stratigrapher attempts to correlate the data derived from several wells.

Well logs

The accuracy of a stratigrapher's predictions and of a geologist's eventual prognostication of petroleum in a particular location is dependent to a large degree on accurate well logging. Several different kinds of logs are utilized, each supplying the petroleum geologist and industry with specific kinds of information. Most commonly used are drillers' logs, sample logs, time logs, electrical logs, radioactivity logs, and acoustic logs.

Drillers' logs

The driller's log provides the most common and basic information to the stratigrapher. It is a record kept by the driller of the depth, kind of rocks, fluids, and anything else of interest that he notices while drilling a well. Particularly when beds are alternating from soft to hard rock, a driller's log may be a very useful tool to geologists. It keeps track of exactly how long it took to drill through a particular bed, and that time record can be correlated with wells drilled later. An astute driller learns to recognize key beds as he drills in an area and to report them on the log.

Sample logs

Sample logs are logs that trained geologists put together from well cuttings and cores: in these, the lithologic sequence and key beds are identified by examining the samples that the drillers provide. A core is the most useful to stratigraphers, because it is a slender column of rock that extends from the beginning of the well to its end, showing the sequence of rocks as they appear within the earth. Cuttings are less useful, simply because the sample is not continuous. If one section of rock extends a great distance through the core, geologists divide that section by its fossils, mineral analysis, and other means. Because it is much easier and less expensive to identify strata by lithologic sequence, other tests are used only when geologists cannot identify by examination everything they need to know. One other common use of cores is to test them for porosity, permeability, and the amount of fluids they contain—that is, their saturation. Beds can often be correlated by these factors as well as evaluated for their oil-bearing potential.

Electric logs

Electric logs record the conductivity of the interstitial water in the rock; they also record the movement of the drilling mud into porous beds or the movement of formation water into the wellbore. Because oil and gas have electrical conductivity properties different from water, the electrical log shows various anomalies that can be used to correlate oil and gas occurrence. The variations are recorded as a sawtooth silhouette on a strip log, and these logs are compared as the basis for correlation (fig. 2.15).

Temperature curves show the presence of oil and gas; water and oil in contact with drilling mud heat up faster than the enclosing rock and raise the temperature opposite the porous strata. On the other hand, expanding gas cools the mud, and this fact, too, is recorded.

Radioactivity logs

A radioactivity log records the natural or induced radioactive characteristics of subsurface formations. A substance is radioactive if it emits alpha, beta, or gamma particles. A radioactivity log, also known as a radiation log, normally consists of two recorded curves: a gamma-ray curve and a neutron curve. Both give an indication of the types of rocks and the types of fluids contained in the rocks. The two logs may be run simultaneously and in conjunction with a collar locator in a cased or uncased hole.

Acoustic logs

Acoustic or sonic logs can be used to determine the porosity of a formation. Such logging tools measure the time it takes for a sound impulse, which the tool generates, to travel through a given length of rock. The speed with which the impulse moves through the rock depends on the composition of the rock and the fluids it contains. By interpreting sound travel times, loggers can determine a rock's porosity. Since oil and gas reservoirs occur in porous rocks, porosity measurements can be helpful in finding potential reservoirs.

Maps

Once the data are determined from the examination and correlation of cuttings and core samples and wireline logs of various kinds, this information is used to prepare many kinds of maps and cross sections.

Contour maps

A contour map consists of a number of contours, or lines on which every point is at the same elevation above or below sea level, of a given area. A structure contour map is used to depict subsurface features (fig. 2.16). Contour lines must be at regular depth intervals

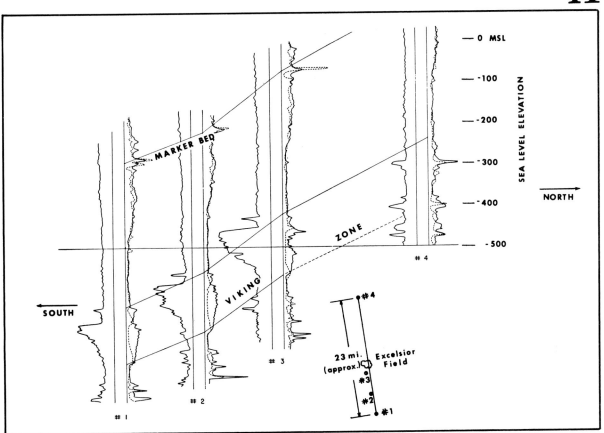

Figure 2.15. Geological correlation
by means of electric logs

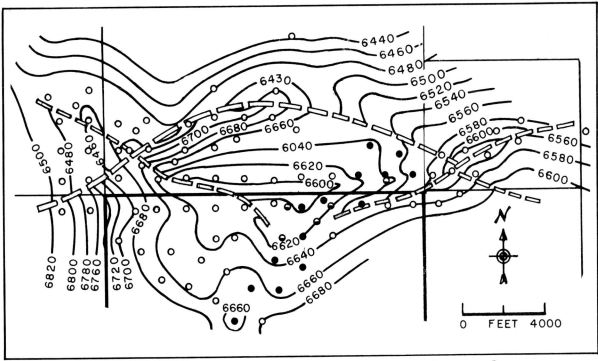

Figure 2.16. Structure contour map

42

to enable the geologist to depict three-dimensional shapes so that they stand out clearly. Other contour maps can be made to show fault attitude and intersections with beds and other faults, as well as showing porosity, permeability, and structural arrangements—such as old shorelines, pinch-outs, or truncation of beds.

Isopach maps

An isopach map shows the variations in thickness of a given formation underlying an area (fig. 2.17). It is widely used in the calculation of reserves, in planning secondary-recovery projects, and in general exploitation work.

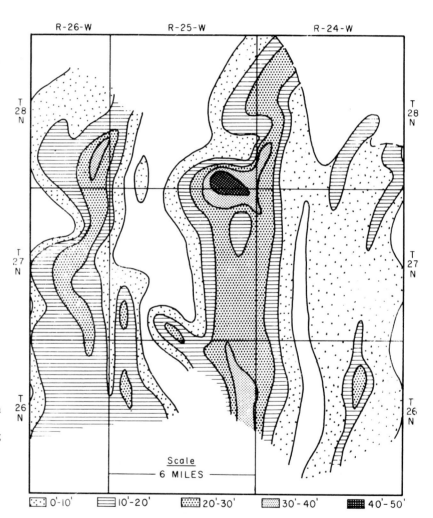

Figure 2.17. This simplified isopach map shows the thickness of residual porosity based on microlog surveys in one subzone. Note the marked trend of the reservoir porosity, its length of some 15 to 20 miles, and its thickness of up to 50 feet.

Scale
6 MILES

⊡ 0'-10' ⊟ 10'-20' ▨ 20'-30' ▧ 30'-40' ▦ 40'-50'

Cross sections

Maps are supplemented by vertical cross sections that show the structure, the fault pattern, or other sorts of details. Maps and cross sections may always be used together to great advantage (fig. 2.18).

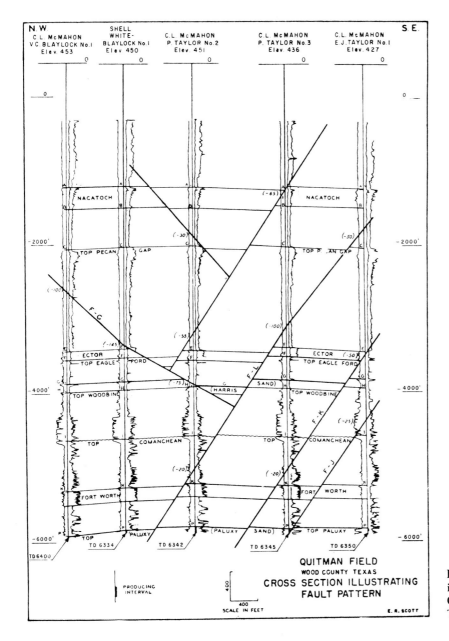

Figure 2.18. This cross section illustrates the fault pattern of Quitman Field in Wood County, Texas.

CONCLUSION

Exploration for oil and gas is often tough work, although technology has made the job of the petroleum geologist and geophysicist much easier. The tools available to the corporation in search of oil are as basic as drillers' logs and as sophisticated as the latest lunar experiments monitoring the earth's magnetic and gravitational properties from space. The continuing development of the industry depends on finding petroleum, and the challenge of doing so is one of the most exciting and arduous tasks of the business.

Aspects
II
of
Leasing

t he worldwide energy crisis requires a conscientious effort on the parts of nations, states, corporations, and individuals to allocate the nonrenewable energy resources as carefully and as advantageously as possible. Individual landowners, states, and the federal government all realize the potential worth of their mineral resources. Mineral rights or leases, which once sold for next to nothing, are now very expensive to acquire. Recoverable resources are vastly reduced, and rising costs of exploration, drilling, production, and marketing make the process of discovering a profitable mineral resource a very risky business indeed.

For example, Chevron, credited with a major discovery of a productive new oil zone in central Alberta, spent about three years doing geophysical and geological research before acquiring enough leases in 1975 and 1976 to test out practically what they suspected in theory was there. Having invested a record Canadian fee of $20,557 an acre for the lease rights to a 640-acre tract, Chevron's wait to see whether drilling would yield a commercially feasible field was a critical one. In this case, it was a productive discovery, but dry holes or commercially unprofitable discoveries are also common.

In order to understand the petroleum industry today and how it relates to the government and the consumer, it is necessary to find out a little about the leasing aspect of the business. Before exploration, drilling, and production can take place, petroleum corporations must acquire leases, either from private property owners or from state or federal governments.

Property owners, both public and private, are increasingly chary of granting mineral leases, and undiscovered profitable reserves are shrinking daily, thereby making the acquisition of new leases more difficult now than in the past. However, the petroleum industry has experts called landmen whose jobs are acquiring leases. The landman must be familiar with the legal side of the question as well

Figure 3.1. The landman's job of acquiring leases includes convincing a reluctant landowner that it is to his advantage to allow mineral exploration and possible production on his property.

as with the social complexities of convincing a perhaps reluctant property owner that it is to his advantage to allow mineral exploration and possible production. In general, the landman has to deal with two kinds of property: public and private. The laws that govern leasing of the two are very different.

THE PRIVATE PROPERTY OWNER'S LEGAL RIGHTS

According to old English common law, a landowner who had the title to a piece of fee simple property could do just about anything he wanted with that land as long as he did not violate the laws of the state. American law adopted this view, and the result is that an *owner in fee simple* (hereinafter referred to as the *landowner*) is pretty much king (or queen) of the land. He owns not only the surface, but also the minerals underground. Until the federal and state governments established certain restrictions to protect the rights of adjacent property owners and to establish conservation regulations protecting the overall hydrocarbon resources of the country, the landowner had unlimited power to drill, produce, and dispose of all oil and gas he could take from his fee simple land.

Today, the landowner still has the exclusive right to search for and remove oil and gas from his property; however, most landowners are not financially able to expend the enormous sums required to drill and produce. Hence, the landowner might lease or sell his rights or a portion of them to someone else. The rights, or legal interests, that primarily concern the petroleum industry are the mineral rights, specifically the rights to the oil and gas contained in the subsoil or to the proceeds therefrom. The three most common options are a lease interest, a mineral interest, and a royalty interest.

Lease interest

The oil and gas lease is a written agreement between the landowner (the lessor) and the oil or gas company (the lessee), which grants the company subordinate legal interests in the landowner's property while it reserves certain rights for the landowner. The company's interests are not equivalent to the landowner's in that the company does not have rights of ownership, but simply those separate rights that are explicitly set out in the lease contract, and those rights revert to the landowner at the end of the lease term.

The company is usually granted exclusive right to enter the land, to prospect for oil or gas, and to remove any that is found there. The lease is granted for an explicit period of years, called the *primary term* of the lease, and for as long afterward as oil or gas is found in paying quantities.

Figure 3.2. A royalty interest may be created either by the landowner's reserving the royalty rights in some way or by deeding them to another party.

The landowner reserves certain rights and privileges when executing the lease: (1) the right to receive a bonus payment for granting the lease; (2) the right to receive delay rentals for each period of time the company retains the lease without drilling or producing royalties; (3) if productive, the right to receive royalty payments according to the terms of the agreement; (4) the reversion of the rights granted in the lease in the event of nonpayment of bonus or rentals, if any are due, or in case production ceases during the primary term or extended term of the lease; and (5) the right to use the land surface as long as such use does not interfere with production.

Mineral interest

A landowner may create a mineral interest in two ways: (1) he may sell the rights to some or all of his minerals to someone else, or (2) he may sell the land and keep some or all of the mineral interests himself. He may do this either by a conveyance, a legal document by which title to property is transferred, by a deed, or by devise under a will. A landowner transfers the rights to the minerals themselves—the mineral interest—by executing a *mineral deed.*

If a landowner sells the surface of his land but retains any portion of the mineral rights, he becomes a *mineral-estate owner,* and the person who buys the land without mineral rights becomes a *surface owner.* The rights of the mineral-estate owner and the surface owner depend on the state in which the property is located and the minerals detailed in the sale agreement.

State laws vary as to whether ownership of mineral rights is "absolute" or not. For example, Texas is a so-called absolute ownership state, and Louisiana is a nonownership state. A surface owner of land in Texas or another absolute ownership state owns the rights to the surface of the land. The mineral-estate owner owns the rights to any minerals detailed in the contract. In a nonownership state, the surface owner owns all, with mineral rights subject to prescription for a specific term; that is, he can grant a lease for specified minerals for a given length of time, and, if not drilled or mined, all rights revert back to the surface owner.

In both absolute ownership and nonownership states the mineral-estate owner has a separate estate from the surface owner. His rights are not affected if the surface owner sells his property or if the surface land changes hands because of a mortgage foreclosure, as long as the severance of the mineral estate from the surface estate took place before the surface mortgage was signed. The new owner of the mineral interest has the same rights as did the original owner as far as his powers to dispose of the minerals are concerned. He may search for oil or gas himself; or lease his undivided interest; or ask for and receive a bonus, yearly rentals, and royalties in the event of production. In short, he may do all things, provided the surface owner has not reserved some of the rights in the original mineral-rights agreement.

The original mineral-rights agreements, because they were not specific concerning which minerals could be removed, started a chain of court cases beginning with Acker v. Guinn (464SW2nd 348 Tex Supp. 1971). Usually, the right to drill and remove product is the right of the mineral-estate owner who can use the surface of the land as is reasonably necessary to remove that product with due regard to the rights of the surface owner. If material damage is or will be done to the surface, the surface owner can sue for damages or take to court to prevent damages (as in the case of Acker v. Guinn where iron ore was the mineral being questioned).

In many of the older mineral leases, oil and gas were implied as the minerals; however, iron ore, lignite, and other minerals are being mined under these leases to the detriment of the surface owner. As a result, the courts are tending to be very discriminating in what they determine as a mineral. In the wake of recent court decisions, the lessee and lessor should avoid complications in the language of their lease by specifically naming the minerals involved. Likewise, the seller and purchaser of the mineral estate should spell out precisely the generic names of the minerals being sold, or bought, in the language of their mineral deed.

State laws

Language of the lease

Royalty interest

Another option the landowner might choose is to transfer only the rights to the *proceeds* from the minerals (rather than selling the minerals themselves) by means of a royalty deed. (The term *royalty* means a share of the gross production free of all costs of production. The term *royalty deed,* often used inaccurately to mean mineral deed, does not convey a mineral title; rather it conveys the rights to the proceeds of the minerals.)

The difference between the mineral-estate owner and the *royalty owner* of a piece of land is that the royalty owner has no right to enter the land or to lease the land for mineral development and no right to the bonus and rentals under a lease. On the other hand, the royalty owner does not have to develop the property or pay delay rentals as the oil or gas leaseholder must. If production does occur, the royalty interest guarantees its owner a stipulated fraction of the gross production, free of production costs and free of a fractional interest in his royalty.

LEASING OF FEDERAL AND STATE LANDS

A large share of total U.S. resources in oil and gas is located on federal or state lands, some of which can be leased to the petroleum industry for exploration and production. The federal government's leasing procedures, which are under the control of the U.S. Department of the Interior (USDI) and the Bureau of Land Management (BLM), are determined by three major objectives: orderly and timely resource development; protection of the environment; and fair market rental from the federal estate. The procedures for leasing onshore oil and gas were set up in the Mineral Lands Leasing Act of 1920; the method of Outer Continental Shelf (OCS) leasing is governed by the OCS Lands Act of 1953–1954.

Onshore oil and gas leasing

Under the Mineral Lands Leasing Act of 1920, onshore gas and oil areas are leased under both competitive and noncompetitive methods. Competitive leases of up to 640 acres and five years' duration are granted for lands located on a known geological structure. Noncompetitive leases of up to 2,560 acres and ten years are granted if the land is not on a known geological structure and has no previous leasing history: in this case, the land is leased to the first person who asks for it and pays the filing fee in what is known as the over-the-counter method. If someone has asked to lease the land before, the BLM lists the tract in a monthly publication, and any U.S. citizen or corporation can turn in one bid per tract. The lessee is chosen by a drawing if there is more than one bid; if there is only one, then that lessee gets the tract; if no bids, then the tract returns to the status of being leased to the first bidder that asks for it.

A corporation or individual is limited by law to leasing a total of 246,000 acres in every state but Alaska, where 300,000 acres may be leased in the north and in the south. Further provisions allow for extending the terms of competitive and noncompetitive leases by two years if drilling is already underway at the end of the primary leasing period.

Competitive leasing to acquire any particular tract is usually done through bonus bidding (fig. 3.3). Sealed bids are generally based on

Form 4–1312 (December 1960)	FORM APPROVED BUDGET BUREAU NO. 42–R1366

UNITED STATES
DEPARTMENT OF THE INTERIOR
BUREAU OF LAND MANAGEMENT

BID FOR COMPETITIVE OIL AND GAS LEASE

The following bid is submitted for competitive oil and gas lease on the lands identified below:

Name of Oil and Gas Field

State	Date of Sale		
Parcel Number of Land Description	**AMOUNT**		
	Total Bid	Per Acre	Submitted with Bid

THE UNDERSIGNED CERTIFIES THAT

a. Bidder is a citizen of the United States *(check one):*   Corporation or other legal entity *(specify kind):*

   Native born   Naturalized

b. Bidder is   is not   the sole party in interest in this lease.

c. Bidder's interests, direct and indirect, in oil and gas leases, offers to lease and options in the above State do not exceed 246,080 acres, including the acreage covered by this bid, of which not more than 200,000 acres are under option. If this bid is submitted for lands in Alaska the bidder certifies as above that his holdings in each of the Alaska leasing districts do not exceed 300,000 acres of which not more than 200,000 acres are under option in each said district.

_____
(Signature of Bidder)

_____
(Address of Bidder)

_____
(City and State)

Figure 3.3. The Bureau of Land Management uses this type form as an invitation to bid for competitive oil and gas leases.

(1) a competitively bid bonus with fixed royalty and rental rates or (2) a competitively bid royalty with a fixed rental rate and fixed bonus. The choice of method is left up to the Secretary of the Interior. Once the tract is acquired, the leaseholder does not have to meet any diligence requirements: he can keep the tract as long as there is some production before the end of the primary term, which can be extended by two years if drilling is underway during the end of the primary term and the beginning of the secondary term.

Historically, most onshore oil or gas lands have been leased on a noncompetitive basis. For example, more than 90 percent of the onshore gas and oil leases allocated in 1972 were allocated noncompetitively, according to a 1974 report on mineral development of federal lands prepared by a U.S. Senate subcommittee.

Annual rental for noncompetitive leases is usually far below those for competitive leases. The royalty fees for production can be as high as 25 percent and as low as 12.5 percent.

OCS leasing of oil and gas

The federal government through the BLM has established guidelines to the leasing of lands on the Outer Continental Shelf (OCS) (fig. 3.4). The guidelines are based on the national energy picture and expected excess demand for gas and oil. They attempt to set out a system that will incorporate the federal government's goals of environmental protection, resource development, and fair rent while establishing a workable system for leasing. The BLM, after considering which of its lands should be leased in what order, notifies the petroleum industry that certain tracts are open for investigation. When the oil and gas companies have obtained seismic data on some or all of the tracts, then an environmental impact statement is prepared and a hearing is held. After further investigation, the U.S. Geological Survey sets a dollar value for each tract and establishes a minimum acceptable bid. The details of the terms of sale for each tract are published at least a month before the date of the sale in the *Federal Register*. The BLM accepts all high bids and makes the final sales decisions (fig. 3.5).

The general terms of the BLM's leasing are determined by the OCS Lands Act of 1953–1954. The tracts must not exceed 5,760 acres, and leases are granted for a primary term of five years and for as long thereafter as oil or gas is extracted in commercial quantities. A minimum royalty rate is 12.5 percent of the market value of all petroleum saved, removed, or sold, and an annual rental is charged for each acre leased.

Although OCS oil has contributed only 5 percent of domestic production until now, it contains over 20 percent of national reserves. One problem with OCS oil is that exploration, development, and production are so expensive that only the major firms can

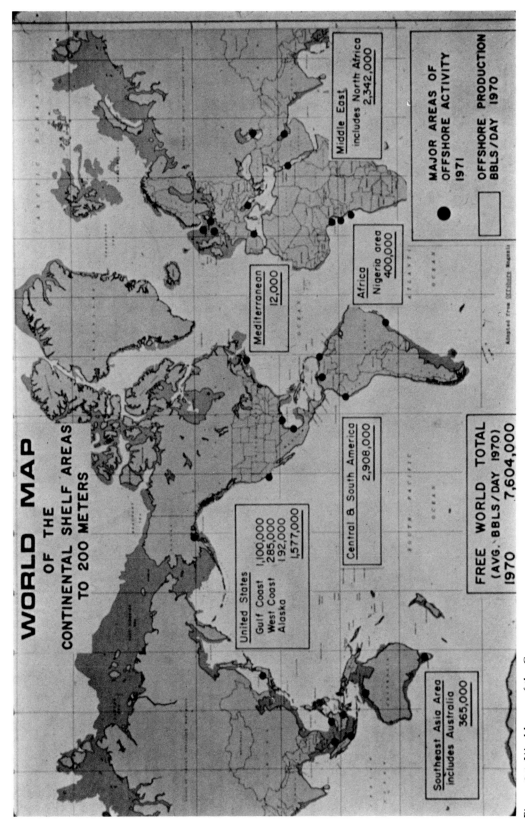

Figure 3.4. World map of the Continental Shelf areas to 200 meters
(Courtesy of American Petroleum Institute)

afford to bid: there is so much risk involved with the high cost of exploration and the high bonus percentage that smaller firms cannot afford to consider bidding. The environmental risks are much greater, but so are the possibilities of a major find (fig. 3.6).

Figure 3.5. An oil and gas lease sale in progress *(Courtesy of American Petroleum Institute)*

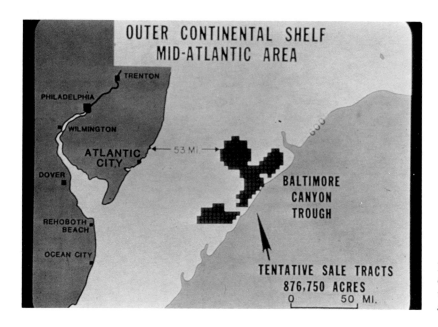

Figure 3.6. Tentative sales tracts include 876,750 acres of Outer Continental Shelf in the mid-Atlantic area.

OBTAINING A VALID LEASE

Of the three methods available to landowners and petroleum companies, the one most commonly employed for securing the rights to mineral production is the oil and gas lease. Because leasing is absolutely essential to the petroleum industry, a sound knowledge of lease laws and leasing practices is necessary for a basic understanding of the field.

Evolution of oil and gas leasing

In the first half of the nineteenth century, before oil was discovered in Titusville, Pennsylvania, the leasing agreements between prospectors and landowners were extremely simple. One lease made in 1853 gave the oil company the rights to "dig or make new springs," the cost of which would be deducted "out of the proceeds of the oil, and the balance if any, to be equally divided . . ." between the oil company and the landowner. "If profitable" is the concluding statement of the agreement, and the phrase reveals the uncertainty of the whole venture.

The first leases

The length of the contract is also significant: both parties agreed that five years was sufficient time to discover and develop any resources that happened to be under the land. Prospecting was luck, not science; and, if petroleum was not discovered within a relatively short time span, it was universally believed that the oil and natural gas would "migrate" somewhere else, thus making further exploration unprofitable in any case.

Early court rulings

As scientists slowly discovered more about the natural laws that govern the behavior of oil and natural gas, some of the stranger theories concerning the migration of these resources were disproved. Landowners, who had thought their chances of profiting from an oil or gas lease were severely diminished if the company did not begin exploration and production immediately upon signing the lease, could not sue oil companies for forfeiture of the lease agreement on those grounds after 1875. Before that date, the courts had upheld landowners' claims that their lease rights included an "implied covenant" with the lessee, which required the oil operator to develop or release the leasehold at once.

Later court rulings

The courts, having heard endless litigation over the migration of oil and gas, finally decided that oil and gas are the property of the person who first captures the resource and reduces it to his control. The language of the hunt, "capturing" oil and "reducing it to the owner's control," comes from the old theory of oil and gas as migratory resources that might wander again onto one's property and then leave—almost like animals. The courts decided it was not their province to judge whose property the oil may have migrated from; the person who drilled a well and found oil was the legal owner. Although it seemed like a reasonable decision at the time, the consequences of the court rulings were not all fortunate.

One consequence of the decision was the landowner's freedom from liability for drainage of a common reservoir even though part of the oil may have lain under a neighbor's land. This so-called *rule of capture* in effect provided the owner of a tract with the option of drilling as many wells as he could, provided he avoided diagonally drilling onto his neighbor's property. The rule does not give the landowner the right to draw a disproportionate amount from the common reservoir because government regulations prorate how much oil can be produced and because the adjacent landowner can choose to drill wells of his own. The *offset drilling rule*, which is an outgrowth of the rule of capture, stated that the landowner whose oil and gas reserves were being drained by his neighbor's wells could not go to court and recover damages or stop the offending operator. The landowner's only recourse was to drill his own wells and produce as fast as he could. The result of both the rule of capture and the offset drilling rule was that operators began overproducing formations in their attempts to drill as fast and produce as much as possible. Many of the formations in East Texas were damaged as a result, and formations elsewhere were in danger as well.

When it proved impossible to provide efficient extraction of oil and gas and equitable distribution of the minerals among the owners under existing legislation, the state governments had to step in and form regulatory commissions to rectify the situation. The state had to consider both its natural resources and the landowner's rights; the resulting legislation attempted to accommodate both interests by enacting comprehensive conservation legislation, well-spacing laws, and proration regulations. The courts and laws are now substantially in agreement on the following points:

1. Oil and gas are minerals and therefore part of the land.
2. When they are brought to the surface, they are personal property.
3. The landowner may drill or transfer his rights to others.
4. The landowner may withdraw oil and gas through wells drilled on his own property without being liable for resulting drainage from his neighbor's property.
5. The landowner is liable for any damages to a common reservoir if he injures the common source of supply.
6. Under some conservation laws, the landowner is liable if he wastes oil and gas by the way he produces it.

Types of owners

The owner of fee simple land has the exclusive right to search for oil and gas and to grant that right to others, provided (1) he has not already granted a lease on the property, (2) he has not disposed of any of the minerals, or (3) he is not under some legal disability preventing him from making a valid contract. Simply stated, not all owners can grant valid leases. Thus, any person or corporation interested in obtaining lease rights to a piece of property has to investigate the legal status and powers of the owner very carefully before investing money and equipment.

Minors

In some states a minor who makes a contractual agreement to lease property can break that agreement if he desires when he attains *majority* (full legal age) at eighteen. Often the law will not recognize leases made by a minor under the age of sixteen, and/or the law may allow minors to void contracts made between the ages of sixteen and eighteen. All states have regulations that control the leasing of a minor's property by his guardian, and some have laws that classify marriage as a way of attaining majority status. In short, it is necessary to examine state laws very closely before entering into a leasing agreement with a minor.

Incompetents

If the person who owns the mineral rights to a piece of property is mentally incompetent, there may be problems in obtaining a valid mineral lease. Some states will not recognize a lease granted by a mentally incompetent person as valid, and other states allow those leases to be voided. Often the decision rests upon whether the person in question has been legally judged incompetent. If the owner of the mineral rights has been legally judged incompetent, then the lessee

58

Figure 3.7. State law must be examined very closely before entering into a leasing agreement with a minor.

should investigate the proceedings carefully before entering into any agreement with the person(s) granted the legal right by the court to make contractual agreements for the incompetent.

Illiterates

The law does not disqualify an illiterate from making a legally binding contract simply on the grounds of his inability to read and write. An illiterate can grant valid leases as long as the proper procedures concerning witnesses, executing the legal agreement correctly, and making his mark are all fully complied with.

Life tenants and remaindermen

A life tenant is a person who is entitled to exclusive possession of a piece of property for the rest of his life but who does not have the legal right to inherit the property. A remainderman is the person who will have full possession of the property after the death of the life tenant and who has legal title to the property.

Because of the joint nature of the interests of life tenants and remaindermen in the same piece of property, usually neither can lease without the consent of the other. Even if both parties join in granting the lease, problems can still arise concerning how the bonus, delay rentals, and royalty payments should be made. Either the arrangements should be written into the lease, or the payments should be made to the lessors jointly, thus eliminating the leaseholder's role in any disagreement between the life tenant and the remainderman over division of payments.

Owners of future interests

Land that is subject to right of use by another party can be leased for oil and gas development if the development does not interfere with the antecedent rights. For example, if the land surface has been leased for grazing purposes only, then the owner could also lease the oil or gas interest and the minerals leaseholder could use whatever part of the land surface was necessary for exploratory operations. The owners of vested future interests fall into the category of remaindermen, and the owners of contingent future interests are often represented by trustees appointed by the courts to represent their interests, particularly in the case of unborn owners of future interests whose oil or gas is being threatened by drainage to neighboring tracts.

Executors, administrators, and trustees

A fiduciary is a person who serves with or without bond to represent the financial, legal, or other interests of the estate to its best interests. Often fiduciaries are attorneys, executors, administrators, and trustees who may be given the power to execute oil or gas leases by the will of the deceased, by a court so that debts can be paid off, or by some special law. The mere power to sell a piece of property does not necessarily include the right to grant oil leases, although the courts have occasionally held that it does. Generally, the power to mortgage the property does not carry with it such additional rights. Thus, executors, administrators, and trustees are not authorized to grant a lease without court approval.

Married persons

The ability of married persons to make legally binding leases depends on the status of their land and the law of the state in which they reside. A husband may execute a lease without the signature of his wife unless her dower rights are involved, but a wife may not have such control over her separate property under many state laws. Although changes in federal and state laws have made it easier for married and single women to have control over their own property, in several states a married woman cannot make a legally binding lease contract without the signature of her husband.

Homestead laws still provide that both parties must sign any document that creates an encumbrance on the homestead property. In certain community-property states, one of which is Texas, the husband is legally the head of the community, and he can grant a lease without his wife's signature on the agreement; however, both signatures are preferred. In others, such as California and New Mexico, and in noncommunity-property states, both parties usually have to sign.

Cotenants

In the majority of states, one co-owner may execute a lease on jointly owned premises without the consent of the other cotenants, but the lease is binding only on the cotenant making the agreement. The lessee acquires the same rights as the other cotenants and therefore can enter the property and search for and produce oil or gas. The remaining cotenants who did not sign the lease cannot be forced to pay for any of the costs of drilling and exploratory operations, but they will share in the profits of production—minus the costs—if the venture succeeds.

Clearing the title

The corporation interested in lease rights to a piece of property must obtain data relative to title, possession, heirship, and many other issues involved in securing a valid, satisfactory lease. Most of the information can be found in various types of affidavits, ratification documents, or deeds.

Affidavits are statements of fact that are sworn to by the maker in the presence of a notary public. Although affidavits are not generally recorded, some that are useful to attorneys examining title to property are required by law and are therefore usually matters of public record.

Affidavit of death and heirship

Affidavit of death and heirship is used by persons when no probate proceedings have been instituted or contemplated. It is preferable that a disinterested third party make the affidavit.

Affidavit of possession

Affidavit of possession is the most important legal document in ascertaining who has proper title. The title examiner depends heavily on this sworn statement to resolve any inconsistencies of defects that may have occurred years ago in the original title. The affidavit must contain facts that are verifiable; not only must the swearer affirm that he is the owner of the property, but also must state the specific uses to which he put the land, whether he lived on it, and so forth. All construction, the dates and extent of it, and the facts for as many years as the person can remember are included in an affidavit of possession.

Affidavit of nonproduction is acceptable evidence to the title examiner when, despite existing records of prior leases affecting the land, it is impossible (because of moving, going out of business, etc.) to locate the past lessee and to obtain a release from him. An affidavit of nonproduction from the lessor and/or depository bank swears that the rentals had not been paid and that the acreage in question was not in production.

Affidavit of nonproduction

Figure 3.8. In most states a lease executed by one co-owner on jointly owned premises is binding only on the cotenant making the agreement.

Affidavit of adverse possession is made by a person who has occupied and laid claim to a piece of land to which he did not originally possess the title. The person who wishes to obtain title by

Affidavit of adverse possession

adverse possession must submit documents that are even more detailed than those necessary for an affidavit of possession. Generally, he must prove he has occupied the land for at least twenty years, and he must take care to satisfy all other specific requirements for adverse possession under his state's laws. In addition to reciting the facts of continuous possession, he must include records of his building a house, living in it, cultivating the land, grazing animals on it, and paying the taxes, submitting relevant tax receipts on the property along with the affidavit.

Affidavit of identity

Affidavit of identity is often required by law or requested by the landman trying to establish a valid lease. The name on the lease must be executed by the landowner in exactly the same way as it was deeded to him. If the deed uses initials, then the landowner swears an affidavit of identity establishing his full name as the holder of the property, and he uses his full name on all lease agreements.

Ratifications

A petroleum corporation is occasionally obliged to supplement and protect a lease that it has already obtained, and one method of accomplishing this task is by securing a legally binding contract that agrees with, or ratifies, the existing arrangement. For example, if it is discovered that the lessor did not own 100 percent of the minerals under the land, the company's landman may secure a ratification of his company's lease by making the owner of the mineral-rights lease a colessor, rather than by going back to the original owner and writing a new lease.

PROVISIONS OF THE LEASE

Once the title to the landowner's property has been cleared, the oil/gas corporation can begin to establish the terms of the lease agreement (fig. 3.9). Over the years, a better understanding of the physical properties of oil and natural gas not only influenced legislation and the court decisions but also changed the basic lease agreements. For the landowner, *drill* or *pay* clauses guaranteeing him a rental fee on the lease regardless of development, and cash bonuses taking into account the location, size, and market value of the leased land became permanent features of the lease agreement. And, for the petroleum producer, clauses granting a definite lease period were added, as were stipulations allowing for deferred drilling if the lessee paid delay rental fees. Most important for the drillers were clauses that asserted the leaseholder's right to continue the terms of the lease as long as the lease was producing. Prior to 1875, a leaseholder had

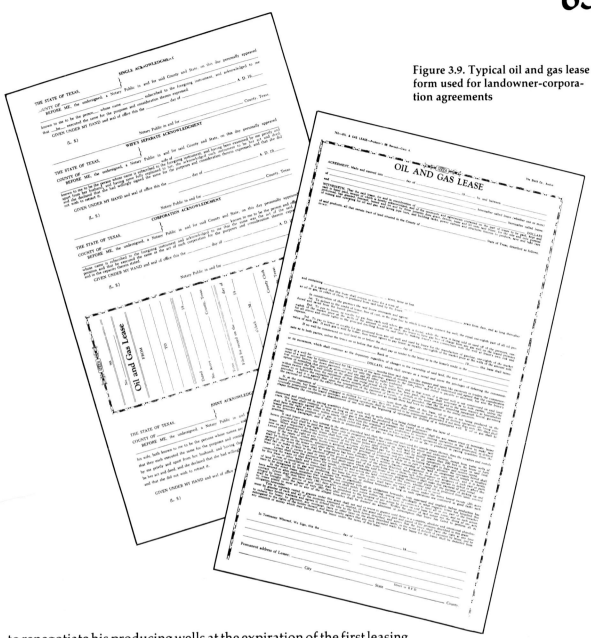

Figure 3.9. Typical oil and gas lease form used for landowner-corporation agreements

to renegotiate his producing wells at the expiration of the first leasing period and agree to the landowner's new price or give up a valuable piece of property. The new contracts were much fairer to both landowners and oil and gas producers.

A lease that complies with these provisions adjusts the relative rights and obligations of both lessor and lessee to the peculiar conditions under which the industry must operate. For example, the lessee has the right to explore when exploration is justified and to terminate the lease when prudence dictates. The lessor receives a cash bonus for signing the lease, his land back within a fixed period if there is neither drilling nor production, and an annual rental for such portion of the primary term as the lease is kept in effect.

Several clauses have become a standard part of most lease agreements: a granting clause, a *habendum* (duration of lease) clause, drilling and delay rental clause, royalty clause, pooling clause, standard clauses outlining the obligations of lessor and lessee concerning the physical operation of the leasehold, the producer's unwritten obligations, and release clauses.

Granting clause

The granting clause of an oil or gas lease sets out the corporation's lease rights and the landowner's rights by naming the purpose and the specific privileges belonging to each party. The sole purpose is usually exploring, drilling, mining, and operating for oil and gas. According to a Texas court, the corporation automatically has the right to enter and exit from the property, to set up equipment, to drill, to carry on secondary-recovery operations, and to reinject salt water into nonproductive formations without any of the above being written specifically into the granting clause. The lessor usually includes a clause requiring the leaseholder to restore the land surface to its original state (as far as possible), and the lessee usually has a clause that allows the company to remove its equipment after operations cease.

Habendum clause

A typical *habendum* clause sets out the length of time for the initial (or primary) term of the lease and establishes that the lease shall be in effect for that length of time and for as long afterwards as oil and/or gas is produced from the land.

The most common *habendum* clause is called the clause of special limitation. It has two parts: the primary term, or exploratory period, ranging from sixty days to ten years, and the secondary term, which can be of indefinite length. Two requirements for production are usually included in the *habendum* clause: (1) production must begin before the end of the primary term if the secondary term is to go into effect, and (2) production must be maintained in order for the secondary term of the lease to continue to be in effect.

Production usually is defined as producing oil or gas *in paying quantities,* and this phrase generally means (1) some profit over and above the cost of any offset well drilled in order to prevent drainage, and (2) any profit above the cost of operation if offset wells do not have to be drilled.

Drilling and delay rental clause

The drilling and delay rental clause of the modern oil and gas lease came about after producers and landowners resolved their differences concerning immediate production or forfeiture of the lease. In the early days of the industry, producers were required to drill within a very short time of acquiring the lease or to give up their lease rights.

The modern drilling and delay rental clause provides the lessee with three options: (1) to drill within the specified time, (2) to pay the determined delay rental fee on the expiration of the stipulated time period if drilling has not begun, or (3) to terminate the lease and thus avoid paying further delay rental fees. Two clauses allow the lessee to terminate the agreement: one requires the producer to drill or pay, and failure to do either automatically terminates the lease agreement; the other requires the producer to notify the lessor in accordance with the provisions set out in the lease if the producer does not plan to drill or pay. The producer may not simply allow the lease to lapse under this second arrangement. One source of conflict between drillers and landowners is solved by the dry-hole clause: in general, producers agree to commence drilling on a second well within a year of drilling a dry hole or to commence delay rental payments; if the lessee does neither, then the lease agreement automatically lapses.

Royalty clause

The royalty clause is an agreement to pay the land or mineral-estate owner an agreed-upon share of all oil or gas produced under a lease. If the producer agrees to pay an advance royalty, he is willing to pay a sum in advance of drilling and to subtract that amount from later royalties. A minimum royalty is the sum that the producer agrees to pay regardless of the actual amount that would be the mineral-estate owner's share according to the royalty agreement. The royalty provision of a lease does not count as a permanent interest in all oil and gas that the land may contain (which would amount to a mineral deed) but instead expires when the lease expires.

Pooling clause

A pooling clause allows the lessee the option of merging the acreage of a given lease with other leases in the area, so that the combined operation can be more efficiently run and wells can be drilled according to well spacing regulations. Pooling is generally used by gas and oil corporations to combine small and irregularly shaped plots of land into one tract large enough to drill a well on.

The mineral-estate owner's lease is not changed in any of the other particular clauses simply by the addition of a pooling clause. The agreement stands as written, and the owner receives royalties on any production that takes place on the combined tract—whether the producing well happens to be located on his property or not. The royalties are divided among the owners in accordance with the percentage of land each has contributed into the pool. Unless there is a specific pooling clause written into the lease agreement, the lessee may not, without additional written consent, combine the owner's royalty interest with other owners' interests, but the lessee may combine his own *working interest* (an agreed-upon percentage) with others if he desires.

Pooling is particularly useful to producers because it eliminates excess drilling—of offset wells, for instance—and allows the producer to develop the tract more effectively with fewer wells and fewer unnecessary delay rental fees. As soon as a producing well is brought in, all landowners in the pool begin receiving royalty payments and all delay rentals cease. Production in one well thus serves to extend all of the leases beyond the primary term, which is also to the lessee's advantage.

Unitization, or merging of leases in all or a large part of the geologic structure in which oil is trapped, is a logical extension of pooling and can work to the benefit of lessors and lessees. The courts have upheld unitization as a power granted to the lessee in advance, particularly when the results of unitization are conservation of the natural resources and elimination of wasteful drilling. Landowners and lessees alike benefit from field-wide planning, which enables companies to maintain pressure thus permitting additional recovery, sometimes to the extent of doubling the amount of gas and oil eventually produced.

Special provisions clauses

Clauses that reserve rights to lessor or lessee concerning the physical operation of the leasehold are usually included in the final agreement. For the landowner, these provisions include restrictions about drilling within a set distance of any buildings, stipulations for the producers to bury all pipe, and agreements for the drillers to pay for any damages to crops that occur specifically because of drilling or producing. For the lessees, the provisions usually include rights to use any oil or water produced on the leasehold for their drilling operations (except, of course, the landowner's water wells or stock tanks); the right to remove their equipment when production has ceased; and the right to know in advance about pending changes in ownership or forfeiture of mortgage for nonpayment, in which case the producer usually reserves the right to buy up the mortgage.

Obligations of the producer

In return for the rights agreed upon in the lease, the lessee normally is considered responsible to the landowner for developing the premises. The obligations are unstated, but they usually include the commitment to drill exploratory wells, to develop the holding after oil and gas have been discovered, to protect the property against drainage by drilling additional wells if necessary, and to carry on purification and marketing operations diligently so that royalties will accrue. All of these implied covenants on the part of the lessee are subsumed under the category of operating in good faith. If the producer does not operate honestly to develop the leasehold, then the usual recourse by the landowner is to sue for damages.

RELEASING THE LEASE

One of three conditions generally causes the releasing of a lease: (1) failure to comply with the terms of the lease, (2) abandonment of rights by the lessee, or (3) surrender of the rights by the lessee. Also, other less common factors might cause forfeiture of a lease.

Failure to comply with the conditions set in the drilling and delay rental clause and/or the *habendum* clause of the lease results in immediate and automatic termination of the lease agreement.

Failure to comply

Abandonment is the lessee's relinquishing his lease rights and physically abandoning the premises without the lessor's consent. In practice, abandonment is usually covered in the provisions of the drilling and delay rental clause and the *habendum* clause of the lease.

Abandonment

Surrender is the lessee's relinquishment of his interest in the rights and physical possession of the lessor's property with the consent of both lessee and lessor. In several states the lessee is under a legal obligation to give written notice of his surrender of the lease, so that the landowner has a clear title and lease record should he want to lease the property again. In the states that require written notice, the lessee can be sued for damages or fined for failure to comply.

Surrender

Forfeiture of property rights by the lessee occurs when the producer is forced to release the lease against his will for breach of contract. The lessor must apply to the courts to obtain a release on his land.

Forfeiture

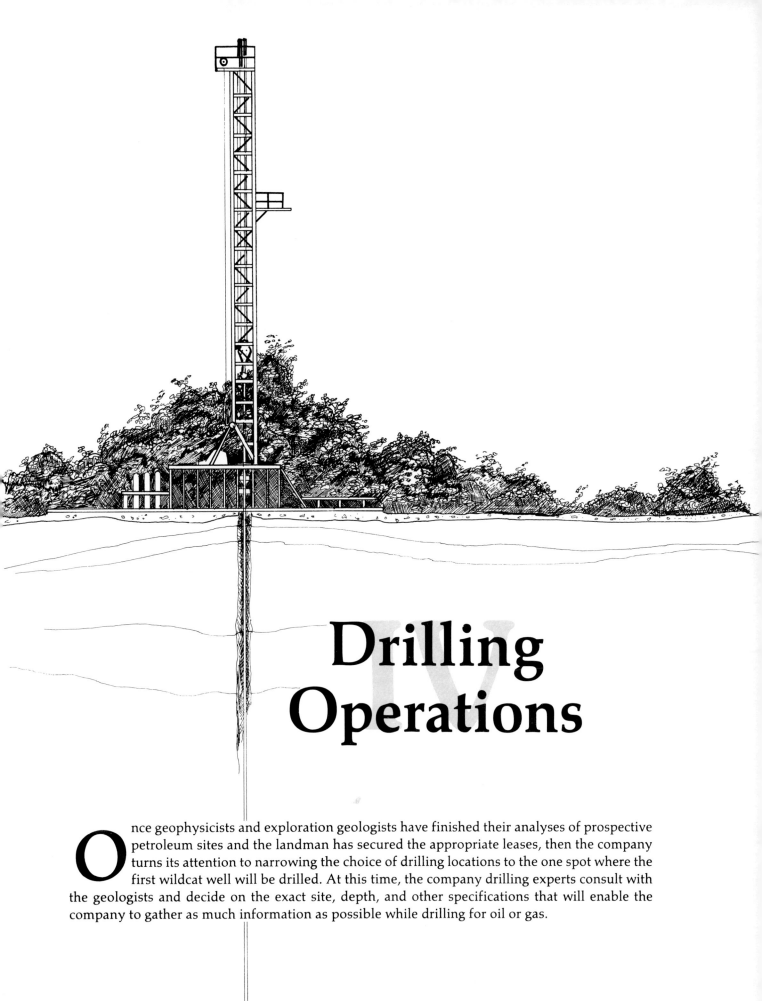

Drilling Operations

IV

Once geophysicists and exploration geologists have finished their analyses of prospective petroleum sites and the landman has secured the appropriate leases, then the company turns its attention to narrowing the choice of drilling locations to the one spot where the first wildcat well will be drilled. At this time, the company drilling experts consult with the geologists and decide on the exact site, depth, and other specifications that will enable the company to gather as much information as possible while drilling for oil or gas.

EVOLUTION OF DRILLING TECHNIQUES

The earliest drillers

In 1857, a New Haven banker, who was also the new president of the Pennsylvania Rock Oil Company, decided that the time had come for the company to send someone to Titusville, Pennsylvania, to turn a headache into a money-making proposition. James M. Townsend had been on the board of directors for a number of years while various schemes to profit by the oil on its land in Titusville had been tried and failed. What the company needed was someone there in person to supervise an even crazier scheme that he thought would solve all their problems: it would drill for oil just as others had been drilling for water. His friends all thought him mad, but he persevered anyway. In December of the same year, he sent an unemployed railroad conductor named Edwin L. Drake to Titusville to set up operations there (fig. 4.1).

Drake, for all his efforts, had a hard time indeed. The method of drilling for water was not particularly applicable to drilling for oil: within 16 feet of the surface, his drillers—when at last he succeeded in finding a crew foolhardy enough to risk time on such an unheard of venture—struck ground water and could not pump it out fast enough to continue excavating in the normal fashion. So Drake had an even stranger idea: his drilling team—a local blacksmith named Billy Smith and his son—would give up digging by hand and try hammering a pipe down into the ground instead. To accomplish this, an oaken battering ram was rigged to a simple windlass (fig. 4.2). By this time, the citizens of Titusville were thoroughly convinced of the foolishness of the scheme and were openly referring to the project as "Drake's Folly."

Even James Townsend had begun to lose faith in the venture. The company stockholders had long since given up hope and were more than a little reluctant to sink any more of their money into the scheme. Townsend had been the only source of capital for months, and in August, 1859, even he sent a final bank draft with which to pay the debts and a letter to Drake to abandon the project. But the driller, Uncle Billy Smith, had not given up hope: he visited the well site on Sunday, just to see how things were doing, and caught a glimpse of something glimmering in the drill pipe. Sure enough, it was oil, and the boom began. Within a few years, the hills surrounding Oil Creek were covered with derricks (fig. 4.3).

Since the days of that discovery, drilling methods have changed drastically. The method of simply hammering away on the end of a pipe served its purpose for the petroleum pioneers, but drilling techniques developed by quantum leaps as men found more and more oil to be recovered. Oil was on its way to being big business.

Figure 4.1 The world's first commercial well was near Titusville, Pennsylvania. Edwin L. Drake, in top hat and frock coat, conceived the idea of drilling for oil and proved his theory with this primitive rig in 1859. *(Courtesy of American Petroleum Institute)*

Figure 4.2. An oaken battering ram and a simple windlass (shown here inside the Drake well reconstruction) were used to hammer the drill pipe into the ground. *(Courtesy of American Petroleum Institute)*

Figure 4.3 Oil fields around Benninghoff Farm in Pennsylvania, 1865 *(Courtesy of American Petroleum Institute)*

Cable-tool drilling

Some of the earliest drilling systems were variations on the cable-tool method. Drilling tools were suspended by a rope or chain cable into the wellbore, and various ingenious—if rather inefficient—methods were used to pound the drill bit into the ground to make hole. Only the lucky ones had engines to do the work. Most people figured out some system that used manpower to raise a pole called a walking beam that dropped the bit and dug out a little more soil. Others managed to contrive a system that enabled a horse to supply the power in a method that resembled a threshing machine.

The tool strings were not very heavy in comparison to the ones used later, and the bit looked something like a funnel: it was about 3½ feet long and about 1½ inches in diameter until it flared into a cutting edge about 3 inches wide. In the course of a normal day, the men would drill for a foot or two, then exchange the dull bit for a bigger reaming instrument, sharpen the bit, and, if necessary, pump out the hole. Then the process would start all over again. It was a very slow procedure, because each time the drillers wanted to clear out excess rock and water from the hole, the whole drill string had to be raised and operations ceased while a bailer or pump cleared out debris.

Modern versions of the cable-tool drilling system are still used, particularly where shallow wells are drilled (fig. 4.4). The power of the cable system comes from the impact action of a bit suspended from a steel drilling cable. As in the old days, the drilled wellbore is almost devoid of fluid because injecting drilling fluid is not part of the drilling system, as it is with the rotary method. Thus, the operator still has to stop to bail out the hole in order to remove cuttings produced while drilling.

Stationary cable-tool drilling rigs with their pyramid-shaped wooden derricks (fig. 4.5) were in use from the 1860s until the 1920s when the portable cable-tool rig became standard.

Early rotary drilling

In rotary drilling, the power of the bit comes from a rotating motion that turns the bit in the wellbore rather than from the impact action of the bit in the cable system. The cable-tool method resembles a man digging with a posthole digger: each thrust loosens the soil by the percussion of the bit hitting the rock. The rotary method spins the bit further and further into the soil, like a dentist's drill, which it resembles in that both drills are lubricated to keep them cool and to flush out excess particles of matter.

The first rotary-designed, fluid-circulating drilling rig was developed in France in the 1860s, but it was less commonly used than the cable-tool rig until someone discovered that a rotary rig with circulating fluid could be used in areas where percussion drilling was not very successful.

Figure 4.4 Cable-tool drilling rig

Figure 4.5. This wooden derrick used by Sun Oil Company in 1919 was typical of the rigs used for cable-tool drilling. *(Courtesy of Humanities Research Center, The University of Texas at Austin)*

The earliest oil explorationists had thought that most petroleum was located under hard-rock formations. This view was supported by the difficulty of drilling with percussion techniques in soft soil: even though the hammering of the cable-tool bit could break up the rock, the splintered fragments closed back around the bit and often wedged it in the hole.

Fluid circulation, which floated the particles of soft rock back up the shaft and out of the way of the drill bit, was an innovation that the Baker brothers developed on their rotary rig in the early 1880s. The Bakers had used their new rig for drilling water wells in the unconsolidated younger formations of the Great Plains. The technique proved equally successful in the unconsolidated soft soil of Texas, where the Corsicana oil field was discovered while the drillers were searching for water. The same equipment, underpowered and not perfected for use in the oil patch, made the drilling of the great Lucas well at Spindletop possible (fig. 4.6). The drillers were farmers, and their tools were minimal, but the techniques proved effective. With the advent of rotary drilling, the oil industry was launched in Texas in a big way. (fig. 4.7).

Drilling today

Rotary rigs are by far the most common in the oil patch today (fig. 4.8). Most are portable—moved in and assembled to drill the hole and then disassembled and moved on to another drilling site. Once the decision is made to stop drilling, the well is completed or it is plugged and abandoned. A system of valves and pipes takes over the production of the well.

Offshore operations of the petroleum industry have resulted in the development of various kinds of submersible and semisubmersible rigs, jackup rigs, and drill ships and barges. Modern-day rigs are equipped with computerized logging instruments, blowout preventers, and a myriad of safety features. Also, a newer drilling technique uses air or gas instead of liquid for circulation, although this method is used on less than 1 percent of the total wells drilled today.

Drilling is usually handled by a drilling contractor, who is engaged by a petroleum company (called the *operator*) and assisted by various companies furnishing services such as the drilling mud, cementing and casing, and well logging.

Experimental drilling methods

Several revolutionary alternatives to conventional rotary drilling are under development and testing. Some of these are the jet erosional drilling system, the continuous chain drill, Stratopax, spark drilling, and the Electrodril system. Of course, these experimental drilling techniques may never come into common practice, but it is interesting to note that research continues in efforts to improve drilling methods.

Figure 4.6. Rotary drilling at Spindletop, near Beaumont, Texas, revolutionized the drilling industry. *(Courtesy of Humanities Research Center, The University of Texas at Austin)*

76

Figure 4.7. Early oil field development in 1903. Note the proximity of the mass of derricks, which was typical of early oil drilling operations. *(Courtesy of American Petroleum Institute)*

Figure 4.8. A modern rotary drilling rig

A drilling system that gained much attention a few years ago was the jet erosional drilling method, which uses high-pressure fluid and metal shots to erode away the geologic structures now drilled by the conventional drill bit. The jet erosional method uses fluid under high pressure and balls of various types of metals to erode away soil and rock at a drilling rate supposedly much faster than the rotary drill. Interest in jet erosional development waned when critics charged that it offered less control over potential hazards such as blowouts. However, research and development of an improved product is currently underway.

Jet erosional drilling

Another experimental method uses a circular chain-link device that incorporates fifteen separate sets of drill bits. The unit is designed to permit rotating a dulled drill bit from its working position at the bottom of a hole and replacing it with an adjoining bit, without having to pull up the drill string. Continuous chain drilling works on the same principle as a continuous clothesline, which permits the user to turn from one clothespin to another as need dictates.

Continuous chain drilling

A prototype drilling bit under development by the U.S. Energy Research and Development Agency (ERDA) and Smith International, the Stratopax combines diamonds and the conventional steel drill bit to give lengthy drilling service. The major problem with Stratopax is finding a secure method of binding the diamonds to the steel bit; reports of a new fusing method are encouraging.

Stratopax

A third drilling method under development is the spark drill, a system that uses high-voltage electric sparking to chip away at the geological formation being penetrated. Projected completion of the research is not expected for several years.

Spark drill

Another new drilling method being tested is the Electrodril system developed jointly by General Electric and Roy H. Cullen of Houston. The system is designed as a modular add-on to conventional drilling rigs. Two basic configurations are under test: a 60-horsepower system designed primarily for offshore directional drilling and a 285-horsepower motor system for use in deep, tough formations. The system reportedly provides greater penetration rates in deep, hard-rock drilling and reduced need for round trips for surveying, bit replacement, and deviated drilling. The Electrodril system has an added advantage because of its ability to sense blowout conditions as they are encountered at the bit face. Reducing the risk of blowouts is important, not only for the company but for the environment as well.

Electrodril

DRILLING CONTRACTS

Before anything else happens in the modern drilling process, today's petroleum operator—be he representative of one of the biggest corporations or a small independent firm—must decide what kind of well he wants drilled and determine the specifications for it. This is particularly important because almost 98 percent of all gas and oil wells drilled in the United States are not drilled by the petroleum companies (called operating companies) that hold the lease rights and will operate the lease, but rather by a contract drilling firm. Therefore, the first job that the operating company faces is to write up an exact list of well specifications for the drilling contract (fig. 4.9).

Contract specifications

In the United States, the customary unit of measure of rig production—or manufacture of hole—is the foot. In many other parts of the world the meter is used in place of the foot; a meter equals about 3.3 feet. The foot is a convenient unit by which to measure the product of a drilling operation and pay the contractor who made the hole. It is a fact of life in the drilling industry, however, that the cost per foot of making hole varies directly with the depth at which the hole is drilled. The deeper the hole, the more costly the foot drilled. Thus, exact requirements are written into the final contract that company and drilling contractor will sign; these include facts concerning the depth of the well, the commencement date, formations to be penetrated, hole size, and casing sizes to designated depths. Even more specific information, such as drilling mud and logging programs, the type of cementing, testing and well-completion programs, and a completion date for the well, can also be included in the contract.

Contract alternatives

Three basic alternatives are available to operating companies considering drilling contracts. They can request contractors to bid on a *turn-key* contract, a *footage* contract, or a *daywork* contract. They might allow contractors their choice and accept bids figured in any of the three ways.

Turn-key contract

A turn-key contract requires the petroleum corporation to pay a stipulated amount to the drilling contractor on completion of the well. In this type of contract, the contractor furnishes all the material and labor and controls the entire drilling operation independent of any supervision by the operator.

Revised February 1976
10M-6-76

INTERNATIONAL ASSOCIATION OF DRILLING CONTRACTORS
DRILLING BID PROPOSAL
AND
FOOTAGE DRILLING CONTRACT — U.S.

TO: HARD ROCK DRILLING COMPANY
1234 Andrews Hwy.
Odessa, Texas 79760

Please submit bid on this drilling contract form for performing the work outlined below, upon the terms and for the consideration set forth, with the understanding that if the bid is accepted by

XYZ OIL AND GAS COMPANY, INC.

this instrument will constitute a contract between us. Your bid should be mailed or delivered not later than ___4:00___ P.M. on ___July 15___, 19___ to the following address:
1312 Wall Street
Midland, Texas 79701

★ ★ ★ ★ ★ ★

THIS AGREEMENT, made and entered into on the date hereinafter set forth by and between the parties herein designated as "Operator" and "Contractor"

OPERATOR: XYZ OIL AND GAS COMPANY, INC.
Address: 1312 Wall Street
Midland, Texas 79701

CONTRACTOR: HARD ROCK DRILLING COMPANY
Address: 1234 Andrews Hwy.
Odessa, Texas 79760

IN CONSIDERATION of the mutual promises, conditions and agreements herein contained and the specifications and special provisions set forth in Exhibit "A" and Exhibit "B" attached hereto and made a part hereof, Operator engages Contractor as an Independent Contractor to furnish the equipment and labor to drill the hereinafter designated well in search of oil or gas on a footage basis.

Contractor agrees to furnish equipment meeting the specifications designated herein, and capable of drilling to the depth indicated herein, including equipment capable of drilling in the water depths herein indicated if this Contract involves a marine operation. Contractor further agrees, subject to all other applicable clauses of this Contract, to provide any and all services required under the specifications stated herein. It is expressly understood and agreed to by Operator and Contractor that when such services are performed on a daywork basis, the performance of such services by Contractor in no way subjects him to liability for any risk not elsewhere assumed under the terms of this Contract. Contractor agrees to perform all work to be conducted by him under the terms of this Contract in accordance with the orders and directions of Operator, with due diligence and care and in a good and workmanlike manner, and agrees to provide competent supervision of the work performed hereunder.

1. LOCATION OF WELL:

Well Name and Number: UNIVERSITY ZX No. 1

Parish/County: Ector State: Texas Field Name: WILDCAT

Well location and land description: Sec. 19, Blk. 34, HID Survey

The above is for well and contract identification only and Contractor assumes no liability whatsoever for a proper survey or location stake on Operator's lease.

2. COMMENCEMENT DATE:

Contractor agrees to use best efforts to commence operations for the drilling of well by the __15__ day of __August__, 19_76_, or within 10 days of completion of site for drilling .

3. DEPTH:

Subject to the right of Operator to direct the stoppage of work at any time (as provided in Par. 6), the well shall be drilled to the depth as specified below:

3.1 Contract Footage Depth: The well shall be drilled to __13,000__ feet or __200' below top of the Ellenberger__ formation, or to the depth at which the __5-1/2__ inch casing (oil string) is set, whichever depth is first reached, on a footage basis and Contractor is to be paid for such drilling at the footage rate specified below, which depth is hereinafter referred to as the contract footage depth.

3.2 Daywork Basis Drilling: All drilling below the above specified contract footage depth shall be on a daywork basis as defined herein and Contractor shall be paid for such drilling at the applicable daywork rate specified below.

3.3 Complete Daywork Basis Drilling: If all operations hereunder are performed at applicable daywork rates, provisions of this contract applicable to drilling on a "footage basis" shall not apply.

3.4 Maximum Depth: Contractor shall not be required to drill said well under the terms of this contract below a maximum depth of __13,500__ feet.

4. FOOTAGE RATE, DAYWORK RATES, BASIS OF DETERMINING AMOUNTS PAYABLE TO CONTRACTOR:

Contractor shall be paid at the following rates for the work performed hereunder.

4.1 Footage Rate: For work performed on a footage basis the rate will be $__6.50__ per linear foot of hole drilled determined by steel line measurement from the surface of the ground if Contractor provides cellar, or from the bottom of the cellar if Operator provides cellar, less footage made in regular size hole while working on daywork basis.

4.2 Operating Day Rate: For work performed on a daywork basis the daywork rate per twenty-four hour day with __6__ man crew shall be:

Depth Intervals		Without Drill Pipe	With Drill Pipe
From	To		
surface	13,500 ft.	$ 1200.00 per day	$ 1440.00 per day
		$ per day	$ per day
		$ per day	$ per day

Using Operator's drill pipe $ - - - - - - per day.

Figure 4.9. A page from a typical drilling contract

80

Footage contract

Under a footage contract, there is an agreed-upon rate per foot drilled. Often this ensures speedy completion of the well because it is to the advantage of the operator and the drilling contractor to get the job done quickly.

Daywork contract

A daywork contract compensates the drilling contractor for days when drilling is suspended and, therefore, no payment is accruing under a footage contract. Day-rate payment is usually written into the drilling contract signed by both parties, and it covers situations in which the drilling rig is on site and performing essential, but nondrilling, operations. Examples are activities like using the drilling rig to take extra cores, perform logging operations, and complete other activities necessary to the petroleum corporation but not compensated in the drilling footage contract.

Combination agreements

Often the bases for payment are combined in the final agreement. A corporation may agree to pay footage rates to a certain depth and then pay daywork rates for any drilling done below that depth. Another common clause included in drilling contracts establishes a *standby* rate, which compensates the drilling contractor for days when his rig is on the site but, for reasons beyond his control, no drilling is taking place. This situation could occur when the contractor is waiting for permission from the customer to start testing operations, for arrival of necessary equipment or supplies, for muddy roads to become passable, and so forth.

Both the operator and the contractor are interested in such details as the time required for completing the job; the safety of the equipment, property, and personnel throughout the operation; and the ability of both the men and the equipment to do acceptable work.

THE ROTARY RIG AND ITS COMPONENTS

A rotary drilling rig may be thought of as a factory, or manufacturing plant. It is designed to perform only one function—*making hole.* A rig differs from other manufacturing facilities, however, in that it is transitory—that is, it must be moved frequently.

The contractor must provide equipment and machinery of sufficient power to drill to the specified depth, yet keep it portable. This equipment and machinery can be divided into four main systems: power, hoisting, rotating, and circulating (figs. 4.10 and 4.11).

81

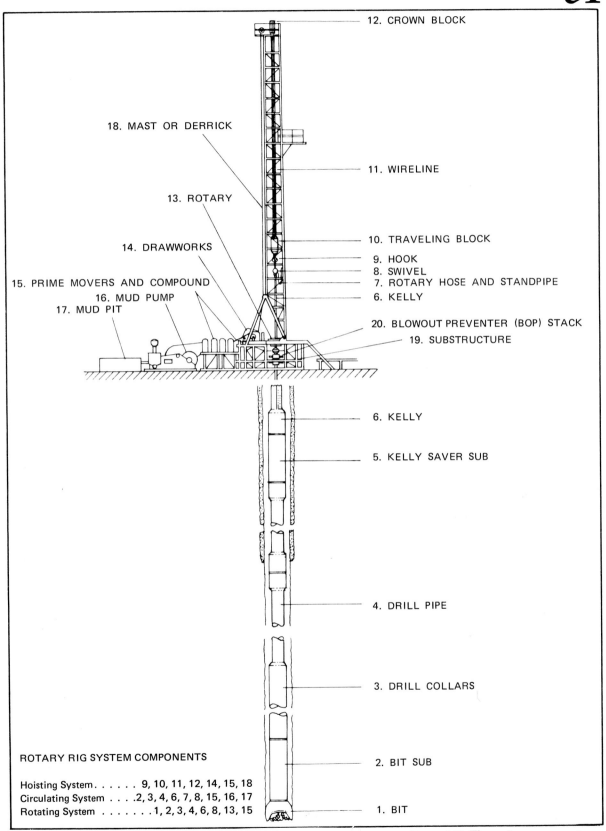

12. CROWN BLOCK

18. MAST OR DERRICK

11. WIRELINE

13. ROTARY

10. TRAVELING BLOCK
9. HOOK
8. SWIVEL
7. ROTARY HOSE AND STANDPIPE
6. KELLY

14. DRAWWORKS

15. PRIME MOVERS AND COMPOUND
16. MUD PUMP
17. MUD PIT

20. BLOWOUT PREVENTER (BOP) STACK
19. SUBSTRUCTURE

6. KELLY

5. KELLY SAVER SUB

4. DRILL PIPE

3. DRILL COLLARS

2. BIT SUB

1. BIT

ROTARY RIG SYSTEM COMPONENTS

Hoisting System. 9, 10, 11, 12, 14, 15, 18
Circulating System 2, 3, 4, 6, 7, 8, 15, 16, 17
Rotating System 1, 2, 3, 4, 6, 8, 13, 15

Figure 4.10. The major components of a rotary drilling rig work together to accomplish its function—namely, making hole.

82

1. CROWN BLOCK AND WATERTABLE
2. MAST
3. MONKEYBOARD
4. TRAVELING BLOCK
5. HOOK
6. SWIVEL
7. ELEVATORS
8. KELLY
9. KELLY BUSHING
10. MASTER BUSHING
11. MOUSEHOLE
12. RATHOLE
13. BACKUP TONGS
14. MAKEUP TONGS
15. DRAWWORKS
16. WEIGHT INDICATOR
17. DRILLER'S CONSOLE
18. DOGHOUSE
19. ROTARY HOSE
20. ACCUMULATOR UNIT
21. CATWALK

22. PIPE RAMP
23. PIPE RACK
24. SUBSTRUCTURE
25. MUD RETURN LINE
26. SHALE SHAKER
27. CHOKE MANIFOLD
28. MUD-GAS SEPARATOR
29. DEGASSER
30. RESERVE PIT
31. MUD PITS
32. DESILTER
33. DESANDER
34. MUD PUMPS
35. MUD DISCHARGE LINES
36. BULK MUD COMPONENTS STORAGE
37. MUD HOUSE
38. WATER TANK
39. FUEL STORAGE
40. ENGINES AND GENERATORS
41. BLOWOUT PREVENTER STACK
42. DRILLING LINE

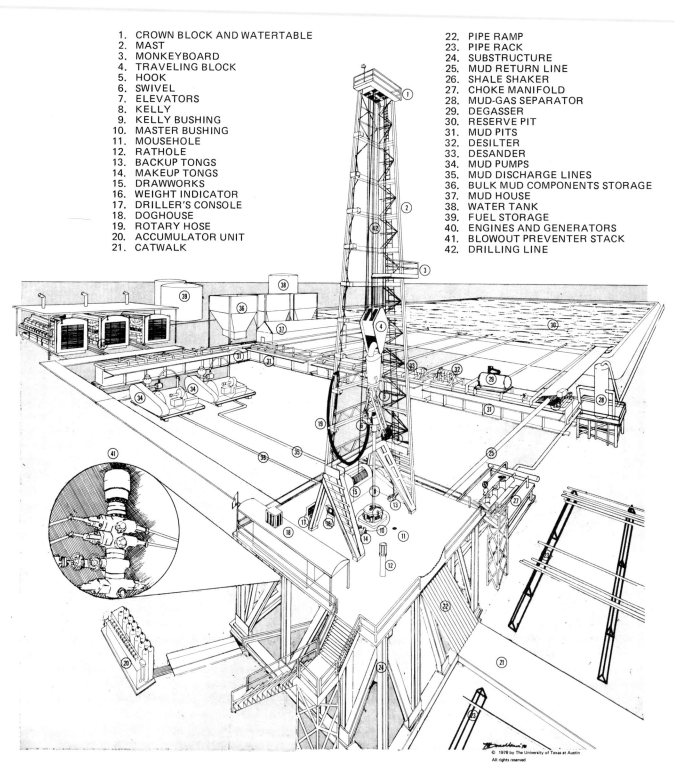

Figure 4.11. The rotary rig and its components

Power requirements for different drilling jobs may vary considerably, but most rigs require from 1,000 to 3,000 horsepower (hp), which is provided by two or more engines, depending on well depth and rig design. Shallow or moderate-depth drilling rigs will need from 500 to 1,000 hp for hoisting and circulation. Heavy-duty rigs for 20,000-foot holes are usually in the 3,000-hp class. Auxiliary power for lighting and the like may be from 100 to 500 hp.

Diesel or gas engines are usually the main power sources (fig. 4.12). Power may be transmitted mechanically from engines through clutches to a unit called a compound, which in turn delivers power through chain drives to the drawworks (fig. 4.13), rotary, and usually via belt drives to the pumps. Torque converters or hydraulic couplings, which depend on fluid drives, are frequently employed in modern drilling rigs. Diesel-electric power units generate and

Figure 4.12. A diesel engine furnishes power for a rotary drilling rig.

Figure 4.13. The drawworks is controlled by the driller.

84

Figure 4.14. The power distribution center on a modern diesel-electric rig

deliver electric current through cables to electrical switch gear, then to electric motors attached directly to the equipment involved—drawworks, rotary table, or mud pumps (fig. 4.14).

Hoisting system

Deep wells are drilled with long strings of pipe and drill collars, the total weight of which is sometimes as much as 500,000 pounds. Long strings of casing also require great hoisting and braking capacities. To accomplish this function, the rig must have a hoisting system. Basically, the hoisting system is made up of a mast or derrick, the drawworks, catheads, the crown and traveling blocks, and the drilling line (fig. 4.15).

Derrick or mast

The derrick or mast supports the hoisting, rotary, and circulation systems (fig. 4.16). Derricks and masts are rated according to the vertical load they can carry and the wind load they can withstand from the side. Derrick capacity figures may vary from 250,000 to 1,500,000 pounds. Most derricks and masts can withstand a wind load of 100 to 130 miles per hour with the racks full of pipe.

Drawworks

The drawworks consists of a revolving drum around which drilling line can be wound; the catshaft on which the catheads are mounted;

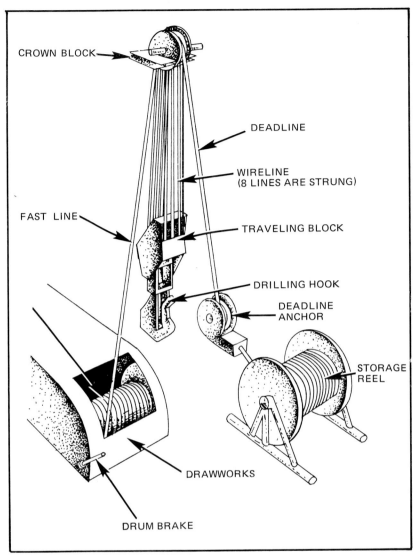

CROWN BLOCK

DEADLINE

WIRELINE
(8 LINES ARE STRUNG)

FAST LINE

TRAVELING BLOCK

DRILLING HOOK

DEADLINE
ANCHOR

STORAGE
REEL

DRAWWORKS

DRUM BRAKE

Figure 4.15. A rotary rig hoisting
system

Figure 4.16. This mast supports the
hoisting system of the rig.

and a series of shafts, clutches, and chain and gear drives for speed changes and reverse (fig. 4.17). The drawworks also houses the main brake, which has the capacity to stop and sustain the great weights imposed when tripping, drilling, or running casing. When heavy loads are being lowered, the main brake is assisted by a hydraulic or electric auxiliary brake to absorb the great amount of energy developed by the huge mass of the traveling block, hook assembly, drill pipe, collars, or casing being lowered into a well.

Catheads

Extending out of each end of the drawworks is a catshaft with a cathead attached at either end. Both ends usually have a *friction cathead*—a drum around which a large rope can be wrapped. With a friction cathead, crew members can move fairly heavy items of equipment on the rig floor. The number of turns around the head and the tension that the crewman applies to the rope creates the friction necessary to develop the required pull.

Inboard of the friction catheads are *mechanical catheads* used exclusively for spinning up or breaking out the drill string during trips and connections. A mechanical cathead is essentially a manual- or air-actuated, quick-release friction clutch and drum to which a tong jerk line or spinning chain is attached.

Many contractors also install small, pneumatically operated hoists, called air hoists or air tuggers, to perform many of the light hoisting tasks on the rig floor that formerly were done with the cathead.

The blocks and drilling line

Drilling lines are made of wire rope, which generally ranges from 1⅛ to 1½ inches in diameter. The fixed end of the rope is attached to the drawworks drum; the other end of the rope is on a storage or supply reel located some distance away from the rig and pipe rack area (fig. 4.18).

When stringing up, the traveling block is laid on the derrick floor, and the free end of the wire rope is reeved, or threaded, over the crown block and through the traveling block using the number of lines suitable for the expected hook loads. The free end is attached to the drawworks drum, and the drum is rotated to obtain a solid layer of turns—one wrap—before lifting the traveling block. Without cutting the line, the spooled end is attached to a derrick leg or anchor device opposite the drawworks.

The line from anchor to crown block is called the deadline (fig. 4.19). String-up generally provides for eight or ten lines from the crown block to the traveling block. The same number of lines are kept throughout the drilling of a well. However, the lines may be increased when drilling deep wells, in order to operate efficiently within the limits of available power, or when preparing to run an especially heavy string of casing.

Figure 4.17. The electrically driven drawworks installed at ground level is supplemented by electric catworks on the rig floor.

Figure 4.18. This skid-mounted reel supplies wire rope for the rig. The electric motor returns the drilling line to the reel when the rig is moved to a new location.

Figure 4.19. A deadline anchor on the rig substructure holds the deadline firmly in place. The loop at the bottom goes to the supply reel.

With perhaps 2,200 feet of wire rope in use as a drilling line, the remainder on the supply reel is used in scheduled slip-and-cut programs that change locations of wear and stress to lengthen wire-rope life. When the line has moved a ton of load over the distance of 1 mile, it is said to have rendered a ton-mile of service. Ton-mile records are carefully maintained in order to employ a satisfactory cutoff program for good service life.

Crown blocks and traveling blocks usually appear smaller than they actually are because of the distance from which they are seen. The grooved sheaves around which the drilling lines passes are often 60 inches or more in diameter. The number of sheaves used on the crown block is always one more than the number used on the traveling block. For example, a ten-line string-up requires six sheaves in the crown block and five in the traveling block (fig. 4.20).

Attachments to the traveling block include a spring unit to absorb some of the shock when handling threaded joints and a hook to support the kelly and drill stem that is suspended from it. The hook shank can be swiveled and usually can be locked in any of several positions to assist the derrickman in latching the elevators when making a trip.

Rotating system

Rotating equipment from top to bottom consists of the swivel, the kelly cock, the kelly, the rotary table, drill pipe, drill collars, and the bit. The equipment between the swivel and bit is termed the *drill stem* although many, especially in the oil patch, still refer to this equipment as the drill string. Technically, the drill string is simply the drill pipe.

The swivel

The swivel assembly sustains the weight of the drill stem, permits its rotation, and affords a rotating pressure seal and passageway for circulating fluid into the top of the string (fig. 4.21). The swivel also has a large bail or handle that fits inside the hook at the bottom of the traveling block. A hose, called the rotary hose or kelly hose, is attached to the side of the swivel, and through this hose drilling mud enters the drill stem.

The kelly

The kelly transmits torque from the rotary table to the drill stem and permits its vertical movement as it is lowered into the hole (fig. 4.22). A triangular, square, or hexagonal piece of pipe usually 40 feet long, the kelly is attached below the swivel with a kelly cock and kelly spinner in between. The kelly cock is a valve used to shut off backflow in case of a blowout. The spinner is used to disconnect the kelly from the drill stem.

The bottom end of the three-, four-, or six-sided kelly fits inside a corresponding triangle, square, or hexagonal opening in a device

Figure 4.20. Drilling line passes through the traveling block (center) and the crown block (at the top of the mast) through grooved sheaves in each.

Figure 4.21. The swivel is attached to the hook under the traveling block with the bail (shown at left).

Figure 4.22. The kelly passes through the kelly bushing, which sits inside the master bushing of the rotary. The kelly is long enough to permit addition of a joint of pipe after the kelly is drilled down. Note the drill pipe in the mousehole ready for a connection.

called the kelly bushing. The kelly bushing, in turn, fits into a part of the rotary table called the master bushing. As the master bushing rotates, the kelly bushing also rotates, turning the kelly, which rotates the drill pipe and thus the bit. Drilling mud is pumped through the kelly on its way to the bottom.

The rotary table

The rotary table, equipped with its master bushing and kelly bushing, supplies the necessary torque to turn the drill stem and accommodates tapered slips for holding the pipe. Slips have teethlike gripping elements that are placed around the pipe to keep it suspended in the hole when the kelly is disconnected during connections and trips. A lock on the rotary prevents the table from turning when desired, as when a new bit is installed on the drill stem (fig. 4.23).

Drill pipe and drill collars

Drill pipe and drill collars are both steel tubes through which mud can be pumped. Drill pipe comes in 30-foot sections, or joints, with threaded sections on each end called tool joints. Drill collars are heavier than drill pipe and are also threaded on the ends. Collars are used on the bottom of the string to put weight on the bit. Rubber protectors can be attached to drill pipe to prevent metal-to-metal contact between pipe and casing, which could cause wear (fig. 4.24).

Drill pipe is a matter of utmost importance to the operating company and the drilling contractor; therefore, the strength and size of pipe are generally written into their contract. The choice of pipe is also governed by hole conditions and the type of drilling to be done.

The bit

At the end of the drill stem is the bit, which chews up the formation rock and dislodges it so that drilling fluid can circulate the fragmented material back up to the surface where it is filtered out of the fluid. Bits are chosen according to the hardness of the formations to be drilled.

The roller cone bit, which is used by most drillers, has two to four (usually three) cone-shaped steel devices that are free to turn as the bit rotates (fig. 4.25). Teeth are cut out of the cones, or hard tungsten carbide buttons are inserted into them. The teeth actually cut or gouge out the formation as the bit is rotated. All bits have passages drilled through them to permit drilling fluid to exit. Jet bits have nozzles that direct a high-velocity stream or jet of drilling fluid to the sides and bottom of each cone so that rock cuttings are swept out of the way as the bit drills. Diamond bits do not have cones or teeth. Rather, diamonds are embedded into the bottom and sides of the bit.

Figure 4.23. The rotary table locks in place, allowing a new bit to be installed.

Figure 4.24. Drill pipe is racked as stands at right. Both plain drill collars and a square drill collar are shown at center. Just above the bit is a reamer. These constitute a packed-hole assembly for straight-hole drilling.

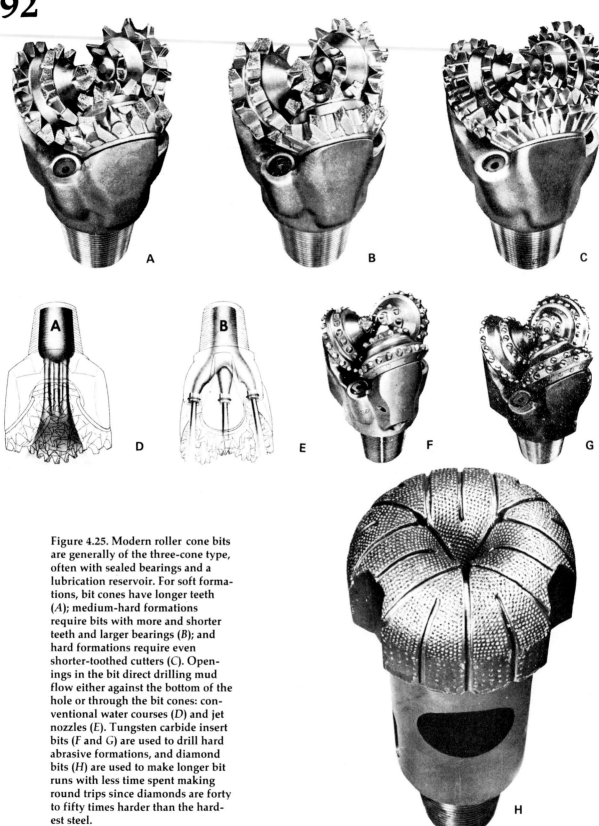

Figure 4.25. Modern roller cone bits are generally of the three-cone type, often with sealed bearings and a lubrication reservoir. For soft formations, bit cones have longer teeth (*A*); medium-hard formations require bits with more and shorter teeth and larger bearings (*B*); and hard formations require even shorter-toothed cutters (*C*). Openings in the bit direct drilling mud flow either against the bottom of the hole or through the bit cones: conventional water courses (*D*) and jet nozzles (*E*). Tungsten carbide insert bits (*F* and *G*) are used to drill hard abrasive formations, and diamond bits (*H*) are used to make longer bit runs with less time spent making round trips since diamonds are forty to fifty times harder than the hardest steel.

Drilling fluid, often called mud, is usually a mixture of clays, chemicals, and water or oil, all of which are carefully formulated to do the best job on the particular well being drilled. Mud accounts for a major portion of the equipment and cost of drilling a deep well. Bulk storage of drilling fluid materials, the pumps, and the mud mixing equipment are placed at the start of the circulating system (fig. 4.26). Working mud pits and reserve storage are at the other end of the system (fig. 4.27). Between these two points the circulating system includes auxiliary equipment for drilling-fluid maintenance and equipment for well pressure control.

Figure 4.26. The mud pump pumps drilling fluid through the circulating system.

Within the system itself, travel of drilling mud is typically routed from the mud pits, to the mud pump, and from the pump through the standpipe and rotary hose to the drill stem (fig. 4.28). Then it goes down the drill string to the bit, up the annular space between the drill string and the borehole, and through the blowout preventer stack to the return flow line. It goes finally to a shale shaker for removal of cuttings (fig. 4.29), then back to the mud pits, which are usually steel tanks. The so-called reserve pits, usually one or two fairly shallow excavations, are actually for waste material and excess water around the location.

   Maintaining the correct consistency and other characteristics of drilling mud requires additional equipment. Mud pit agitators help maintain a uniform mixture of solids and fluids. Other auxiliaries include a desander and desilter for removing fine solids that would otherwise not settle out and a vacuum degasser for quick release of gas that may be entrained in the drilling mud (fig. 4.30).

Circulating equipment

Mud is circulated through a blowout preventer stack, which is located on the well casing beneath the rig floor or on the ocean floor. Also installed with the stack are a line for mud return to the shale shaker, a line to fill up the hole when making a trip, a kill line to pump mud into the hole when needed to restore pressure balance, and lines to the choke fittings for relieving pressures in the wellbore.

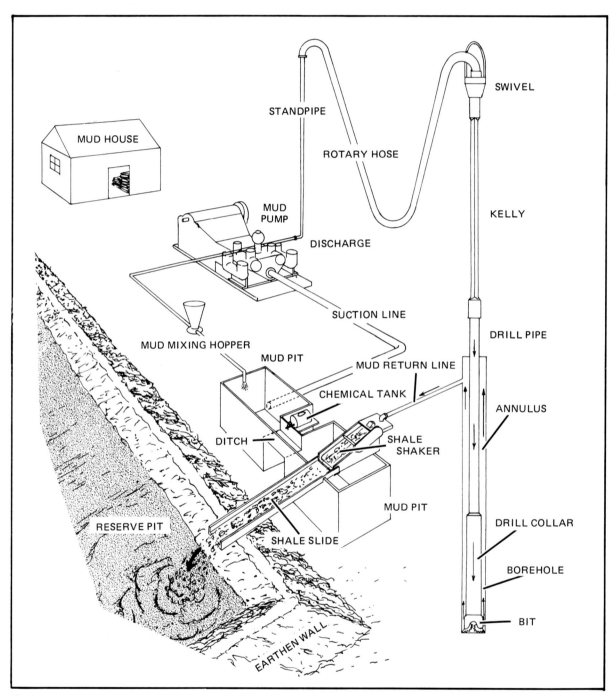

Figure 4.27. The circulating system

Figure 4.28. Drilling fluid is pumped into the swivel and kelly through the rotary hose.

Figure 4.29. The shale shaker, a series of vibrating trays, sifts cuttings from the circulating fluid.

Figure 4.30. Auxiliary circulating equipment includes a degasser, desilter, desander, shale shaker, and reserve (waste) pit.

ROUTINE DRILLING OPERATIONS

Once the seismographs have been analyzed, the leases signed, and the drilling contracts agreed upon, the operating company determines the exact spot for drilling. Then the drilling contractor prepares the drill site to accommodate his rig and equipment.

The land is cleared and leveled, access roads are built, water is made available, and an earthen pit is dug out and lined with plastic to serve as a waste collector. At the exact spot of the borehole, often a rectangular pit called a cellar is dug and prepared to accommodate drilling accessories that will be installed under the rig. In the middle of the cellar, the main borehole is started, sometimes with a small, truck-mounted rig. This hole—the conductor hole—is large in diameter, about 20 to 100 feet deep, and lined with a conductor pipe. If the top soil is soft, the conductor pipe is simply driven into the ground with a pile driver.

Preparing the drill site

Another hole, called the rathole, is dug beside the cellar and also lined with pipe. The rathole is used to store the kelly when it is temporarily out of the borehole. Sometimes, when the derrick substructure is not very tall, a third hole, called the mousehole, is dug. The mousehole extends through the rig floor and is used to hold a joint of pipe ready for makeup.

The contractor then moves in his rig and related equipment so drilling can commence. The process, known as rigging up, begins with the substructure—the framework that supports the derrick or mast, pipe, drawworks, and sometimes the engines. If a mast is used, it is brought to the site already assembled and is hoisted upright from a horizontal position (fig. 4.31). A standard derrick is brought to the site in sections and assembled on location. The components of the support system are moved into place and readied for drilling.

Rigging up

Other rigging-up operations include erecting guardrails, walkways, and stairways; installing auxiliary equipment to supply electricity, compressed air, and water; and setting up storage facilities and living quarters for the toolpusher and company man.

Figure 4.31. A mast is raised to an upright position, using power from the drawworks.

Drilling the surface hole

Once the rig is in position over the conductor hole, drilling is ready to begin. The first bit is large and is attached to the first drill collar, lowered into the conductor hole, with sections of drill pipe added until the bit is on bottom. Then the kelly is attached to the topmost joint of drill pipe.

Every 30 to 40 feet (the length of the kelly) another joint of drill pipe is added to the drill stem. This operation—making a mousehole connection—is accomplished by the use of tongs and a tong pull line or a kelly spinner, which is an air-actuated device mounted near the top of the kelly. The kelly is unscrewed from the drill pipe, moved over the pipe in the mousehole, stabbed into the drill pipe, and

Figure 4.32. The derrickman places a rope around the pipe as it comes out of the hole and racks it in the fingerboard (shown under and behind his right foot).

Figure 4.33. Standing on the heavy-duty slips used to hold the casing string, a casing crewman stabs a joint of casing.

tightened by the crew. The new joint is then connected to that in the hole, while it is being held by the slips. A connection is made each time the kelly is drilled down, that is, each time about 30 or so feet of hole is made.

At some depth when the hole has gone past soft, sticky formations, gravel beds, and the like that lie near the surface, drilling stops and the drill stem is pulled out of the hole. This first hole is known as the surface hole.

Tripping out

Pulling the whole drill stem and bit out of the hole in order to change bits, run samples, or perform some other operation in the borehole is called tripping out. To trip out, the slips are set and the kelly, kelly bushing, and rotary hose are removed from the drill pipe and stored in the rathole. The floormen latch the elevators onto the drill pipe, and the driller pulls the pipe out of the hole. The pipe is raised until it reaches the derrickman located on the monkeyboard high in the mast. The derrickman grabs the stand of pipe with a rope or chain and guides it into the fingerboard (fig. 4.32) as the floormen below disconnect the pipe and place it on the rig floor in an orderly fashion. The pipe is usually removed in stands of three joints at a time. The drill collars and bit are last to come out of the hole.

Running surface casing

Once the pipe is out, the casing crew moves in and runs the surface casing. Casing is large-diameter steel pipe and is run into the hole with the use of special heavy-duty casing slips, tongs, and elevators (fig. 4.33). Casing accessories include centralizers, scratchers, a guide shoe, a float collar, and cement plugs. Centralizers keep the casing in the center of the hole, while scratchers help remove the caked drilling mud from the wall of the hole. The guide shoe guides the casing past debris in the hole, and the float collar serves as a receptacle for cement plugs and to keep drilling mud from entering the casing. Once the casing string is run, it is cemented in place.

Cementing

An oilwell cementing service company usually performs the job of cementing the casing in place. As in running casing, the men and equipment of the drilling contractor are usually available for the cementing operation. Cementing service companies stock various types of cement and use special transport equipment to handle this material in bulk. Bulk cement storage and handling at the well site make it possible to mix the large quantities needed in a short time.

The cementing crew mixes the dry cement with water, often using a jet mixing hopper (4.34). Then, liquid slurry is pumped to a special valve made up on the topmost joint of casing (the cementing head, or plug container). As the slurry arrives, the bottom plug is released and precedes the slurry down the inside of the casing, seats in the float collar, and allows the cement slurry to pass through a passageway in it. The slurry flows out through the guide shoe and starts up the

100

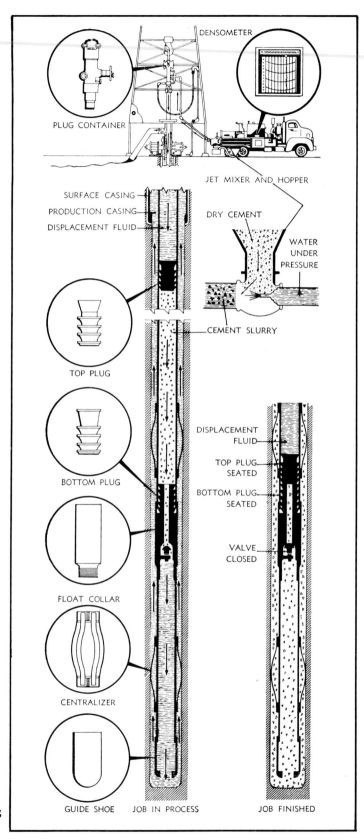

Figure 4.34. Diagram of a casing cementing job

annular space between the outside of the casing and wall of the hole until the space is filled. A top plug follows the slurry down the casing as displacement fluid is pumped in behind it. When the top plug reaches the bottom plug and pumps are shut down, the slurry is allowed to harden. This period is known as waiting on cement or simply WOC. After the cement hardens and tests indicate that the job is good, the rig crew attaches and tests the blowout preventer stack and drilling is resumed.

Tripping in

To resume drilling, the drill stem and a new, smaller bit that fits inside the casing must be tripped back into the hole. Working together, the derrickman, floormen, and driller attach the bit, the drill collars, and each stand of pipe as the drill stem is lowered into the hole. Using a spinning chain, tongs, and a mechanical cathead (the makeup cathead), a new stand is spun into the stand suspended in the hole until the drill stem reaches bottom (fig. 4.35). The drill bit drills through the cement inside the casing, and making hole continues. As formations get harder and drilling progresses, round trips are necessary to replace worn bits and to facilitate testing.

Figure 4.35. Using a spinning chain, floormen spin a new joint of pipe into the stand suspended in the hole.

Running and cementing intermediate casing

At a certain depth, drilling stops again in order to run another string of casing—this time smaller in diameter. This intermediate string runs through the surface string down to the bottom of the intermediate hole. At this depth formations are often troublesome. They could cause a blowout or contain shale that sloughs off and fills the hole.

Drilling to final depth

Using a still smaller bit, the final part of the hole is drilled. The bit and drill stem are tripped in, the intermediate casing shoe is drilled out, and drilling resumes with the pay zone in mind—that is, a formation capable of producing enough gas and oil to make it economically feasible for the operating company to complete the well.

Evaluating formations

To help the operator decide whether to stop drilling or continue, several techniques are used. A thorough examination of the cuttings made by the bit helps the operator decide whether the formation contains sufficient hydrocarbons. The mud logger, usually a person who has training in geology, catches cuttings at the shale shaker as they are pumped out of the well and analyzes them in a portable laboratory (usually a trailer) at the well site. A large number of instruments, many computer operated, are used by the mud logger to analyze well fluids at varying depths as drilling progresses (fig. 4.36).

Well logging is another valuable method of analyzing downhole formations. Using a mobile laboratory, well loggers lower logging tools to the bottom of the well on wireline and then slowly retrieve them. As they pass back up the hole, they measure and record properties of the formations. Electric logs measure and record electricity in formations, while radioactivity logs measure and record radiation. Many types of logs, all resembling an electrocardiogram, are generated for study and interpretation by experienced geologists and engineers to determine the presence of oil or gas (fig. 4.37).

Another technique often used is the drill stem test. A drill stem test (DST) tool, which is made up on the drill stem, is set down on the bottom of the hole where the downhole formation pressure and fluids enter the tool and activate a recorder. The tool is retrieved, and the recorded graph indicates characteristics of the reservoir.

In addition to these tests, formation core samples can be taken from the hole and examined in a laboratory.

Setting production casing

After the drilling contractor has drilled the hole to final depth, and the operating company has evaluated all test interpretations, the company decides whether to set casing or plug the well. The company may doubt that a well will produce enough oil or gas to pay for casing and completing the well, which is a costly operation. If the well is judged to be a dry hole—that is, not capable of producing oil or gas in commercial quantities, the well will be plugged and abandoned. Cost in that case would be much less than completion costs.

If the operating company decides to set casing, pipe will be hauled to the job and tested, and other preparations will be made to run it into the well. Prior to running casing, the usual practice is to get back into the hole with a bit to check for possible bridging and settling of cuttings on the bottom. Generally, the drilling crew will lay down the drill pipe as it is removed from the hole.

Production casing is made up with special care in order to guard against future leaks. Once again, a contract casing crew with special equipment for running and making up the casing is obtained to handle this task.

Figure 4.36. The mud logger examines cuttings in his portable laboratory.

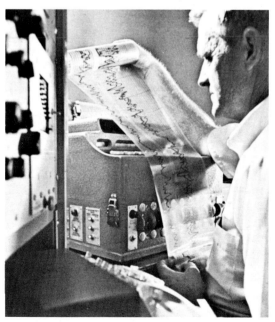

Figure 4.37. An electric log helps determine the presence of oil or gas.

Figure 4.38. Offshore cementing equipment includes a skid-mounted pump unit (left center), mixing hopper (lower right), and a bulk cement tank (upper right).

Figure 4.39. A motion compensator helps keep tension on the drill stem to offset the effects of heave while drilling from a floating foundation.

The drilling contractor nears the completion of his job when the hole has reached total depth and casing has been set and cemented. Usually, he will run tubing, set the wellhead, and bring in the well, following instructions of the operating company. In some cases, the drilling contractor will move his rig and equipment to the next location after casing is cemented in the well. Offshore, cement-handling equipment is usually permanently installed on the rig (fig. 4.38).

OFFSHORE DRILLING

Offshore operations of the petroleum industry began as extensions of onshore exploring, drilling, and producing. By the late 1930s seismic surveys had been made of coastal marshlands, bayous, and shallow bays adjacent to the Gulf of Mexico. In Louisiana, barges sunk in dredged channels with water depths of 4 to 8 feet and secured in position by wooden pilings had proved themselves as drilling platforms. Drilling operations in shallow bays were conducted on wooden platforms mounted on timber piles. Supplies were brought to these operations by barge through access channels or by trestles from nearby shore or boat landing locations. As early as 1900, drilling was done from wharves extending out into the Pacific from California beaches. Most of the early activities in water-covered areas were to extend field boundaries and to recover oil from reservoirs already defined on shore.

Development of offshore drilling

Every advancement away from the solid ground of prairies and dry land toward the open seas brought problems that had to be solved. The usual pattern was for the operator to try the equipment and skills already in his possession; when this was not enough, he had to seek new materials, designs, and methods (fig. 4.39). Successful adaptations of existing resources were quickly imitated or improved by competing operators. The net result has been a fairly steady evolution in every aspect of offshore activity.

As offshore operations move into greater water depths and more hostile environments, all costs increase rapidly. One of the most striking effects is in the increase in size of petroleum reserves required to justify the development of a discovery field. In some areas a reserve estimated at 100,000,000 barrels of petroleum must be considered marginal and await development on that basis. Commercial reserves begin at 300,000,000 barrels of anticipated production for some fields. Other factors that influence rising costs and feasibility of development are increasing participation of host countries in leases, bonuses, and disposition of production.

However, exploration is growing as improvements in drilling and exploratory techniques increase the area where commercially feasible operations are possible. As a result, exploratory drilling has greatly expanded in order to determine reservoir locations and sizes (fig. 4.40). The number and design of drilling and/or production platforms is determined by information obtainable only from the results of exploratory drilling. Production and transportation facilities are not constructed until their need is assured.

The distinction between *exploratory* drilling and *development* drilling is important to the understanding of offshore operations.

Exploratory drilling is done from mobile rigs, and the wells, casing, and hole are abandoned; only in rare instances is the hole reentered. Development wells are usually drilled from fixed platforms with production and well maintenance facilities.

Mobile exploratory drilling rigs

Environment determines which type of the five most common mobile rigs is best suited for a particular job. A company may decide to employ a submersible drilling rig, a semisubmersible one, a jackup rig, a drill ship, or a drill barge. The environment in which each type of mobile drilling rig functions best is determined by its performance in various water depths and in adverse weather conditions. Equally important in the choice of a mobile rig are considerations like the support requirements for the men living on the rig, mobilization problems of getting the rig on location, positioning capabilities, and any problems pertaining to station keeping.

Submersible rigs

Submersible rigs are among the oldest of mobile exploratory drilling rigs, and the idea for them doubtless emerged from the earliest offshore rigs, which were sunken barges secured in place by wooden pilings (fig. 4.41). The obvious advantage of a submersible rig is that it can be moved after the exploration is complete.

The submersible unit consists of two hulls—upper and lower. The upper hull houses the crew's quarters and all working spaces. The lower hull provides the buoyancy necessary when floating the unit from one drill site to another. At the site, the lower hull is flooded slowly until it sinks and rests on the seabed, forming a firm support for the drilling operation.

Once the drilling operation has been completed, the ballast water is forced out of the lower hull and the unit is refloated. Submersibles have limited capability due to the relatively shallow water in which they can work—typically from 30 to 40 feet although some have been constructed that can operate in depths of 100 feet or more. However, submersible rigs are not easily moved, nor is their use feasible except in shallow waters. For this reason, although there are still many submersible rigs in operation, construction of new ones is minimal. The exploratory drilling unit that combines the stability of a submersible rig with the ability to move from site to site is the increasingly popular jackup rig.

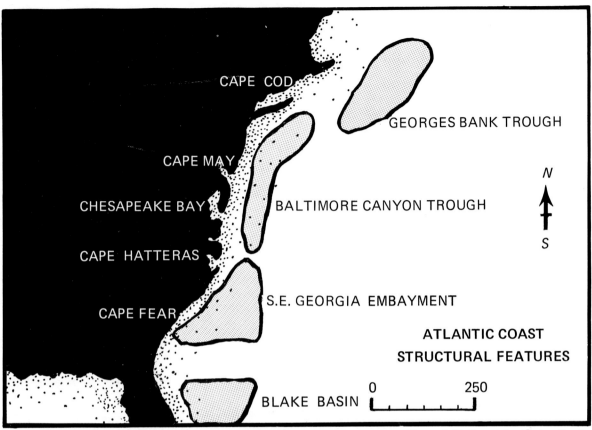

CAPE COD

GEORGES BANK TROUGH

CAPE MAY

CHESAPEAKE BAY

BALTIMORE CANYON TROUGH

CAPE HATTERAS

N

S

CAPE FEAR

S.E. GEORGIA EMBAYMENT

ATLANTIC COAST
STRUCTURAL FEATURES

0   250

BLAKE BASIN

Figure 4.40. Promising Outer Continental Shelf resources are shown on this map of the Atlantic Coast structural features. *(Courtesy of American Petroleum Institute)*

Figure 4.41. This submersible drilling unit at work off the coast of Louisiana is one of the largest of its kind. Note the helipad, or heliport, at left.

Jackup rigs

The jackup rig provides a fixed drilling platform, and its initial cost is less than that of other mobile drilling units. Because of its greater depth capability, the jackup rig is the most widely used bottom-supported, mobile offshore drilling unit (fig. 4.42). Jackup rigs have watertight hulls that serve as a vessel while the unit is towed between drill sites. During transit, the unit's legs are jacked up to optimum height above the hull.

When the jackup is positioned at the drill site, the legs are jacked down until they rest on the seabed. The hull is then jacked above the water's surface until a sufficient air gap exists to permit operations to be carried out unhampered by tides and waves.

The jackup rig is limited to a maximum of approximately 350 feet of water depth since it must be supported by the seabed. However, because the jackup is supported from the bottom, there is little or no vessel motion when drilling, and heave, or motion, compensation is not required. Also, problems caused by violent winds and weather do not affect the jackup rig nearly as much as those that float.

Jackup rigs have several disadvantages that are generally associated with moving and with assembling and disassembling operations. They are difficult to tow, and the legs must be shortened or removed for long voyages. Accidents underway have therefore produced a poor safety record, and going on or off location is hazardous as is jacking the rig platform up or down. In addition, complications are caused by the moving parts of the jacking mechanism, which can break down and cause drilling delays.

Semisubmersible rigs

Semisubmersible drilling rigs came into use as the need for floating drilling platforms (called *floaters*) became evident for drilling in deep water. The first semisubmersible rigs were simply submersibles that had been converted for drilling when floating and anchored on location. The newer ones were more streamlined in order to facilitate towing, and design changes in the buoyancy and flotation chambers increased towing speeds from 3 to 10 knots. An even more recent improvement is the self-propelled semisubmersible rig, which can be positioned when it arrives at the drilling site to help combat drift from wind, wave, and ocean currents.

Keeping a drilling rig over the drill site without the use of anchors or bottom-support structures is known as dynamic positioning. It is accomplished by the use of fast-acting, powerful propellers (called thrusters) driven by electric motors that direct their thrust in the desired direction. Thrusters are controlled by various sensing devices working through a computer.

The semisubmersible rig is a hybrid unit (fig. 4.43). It has a working deck similar to the bottom-supported jackup, but it is stabilized by ballasting its pontoons and columns to a predetermined

Figure 4.42. Three cylindrical legs give this jackup unit its bottom support.

Figure 4.43. A semisubmersible drilling unit floats on hulls that are flooded and submerged just below the water's surface.

depth. An air gap separates the working area from the sea surface. In shallow water, some semisubmersibles can be ballasted to rest on the seabed and operated as a bottom-stabilized unit.

Like the submersible, the semisubmersible's pontoons and columns are deballasted, and the rig is floated high in the water once its drilling assignment is completed. Some new semisubmersibles are self-propelled, and a few are equipped with thrusters to permit station-keeping capability at the drill site.

The semisubmersible is the most stable offshore mobile unit for use in deep, rough water such as the Gulf of Alaska or the North Sea. It is generally satisfactory for water depths up to about 2,000 feet, and it has a good safety record. On the other hand, semisubmersibles have a limited cargo capacity and therefore require more support vessels, such as supply ships and tugboats.

The drill ships and drill barge are two other seagoing vessels that function as offshore drilling platforms for exploratory drilling operations. The major differences between the two are that drill ships are self-propelled and have the appearance of conventional ocean-going ships, whereas drill barges are not usually equipped with a propulsion system.

Drill ships and barges

Drill ships have proven deepwater capability, offer faster travel time to remote locations, do not need tugboats, and require fewer supply ships, since they can carry larger loads of drilling and maintenance supplies than jackups, which often operate in the same water depths (fig. 4.44). However, a drill ship is staffed by a captain and his crew of sailors, who are not involved with drilling operations but only with the running of the ship. The salaries of these people, their maintenance, and the space they occupy on board ship continue throughout the drilling operation.

Drill barges, on the other hand, do not have the additional crew on board because they are towed to the drilling site by tugs and then left there while on location. A barge master and watch standers remain on board to attend to the details of flotation and loading of the vessel. Barges are the least expensive of the floaters because sailors not involved in drilling are not maintained on board. However, barges move slowly since they depend on tugs and other work boats to tow them to location.

Although both drill ships and drill barges are equipped with ballasting systems to provide optimum stability during operations, the major disadvantage of the drill ship is its limited capacity to operate in wind or wave conditions that produce excessive motion.

The first structure specifically designed as an offshore platform was installed in the Gulf of Mexico in 1947 in a water depth of 20 feet. In almost three decades since this beginning the industry has installed

Stationary drilling platforms

Figure 4.44. A drill ship works in calm waters. Note anchor chain windlasses on the bow of the vessel.

Figure 4.45. A fixed platform and its tender are used to drill offshore development wells.

thousands of fixed platforms in water depths ranging to 400 feet. Platforms for use in the North Sea will be installed in 460-foot depths. A Santa Barbara Channel platform will stand in a water depth of 850 feet, and in the Gulf of Mexico one will rest in over 1,000 feet of water.

Approximately two-thirds of the drilling and/or production platforms of the world are located in the Gulf of Mexico. The improved techniques of fabrication and erection gained in the gulf structures have influenced platform construction worldwide.

Fixed platforms (fig. 4.45), whether for drilling or production, must be constructed to withstand environmental forces. Hurricane winds in the Gulf of Mexico, icy Arctic seas in the Cook Inlet, or earthquakes in the Pacific are all factors that dictate both design and construction materials employed. *Environmental factors*

Differences in ocean bottom conditions affect the foundation structures. Pilings that can be used in the Gulf of Mexico, where the seafloor is soft, are inappropriate for the North Sea, where the rocky bottom prevents driving pilings deep into the ocean floor; gravity-supported structures, less dependent on driven pilings, have been used instead. Other areas of the world have still other problems, and the platform is constructed to withstand the location conditions.

A drilling platform is constructed to enable the contractor to drill as many wells as possible from the same permanent location (fig. 4.46). *Construction features*

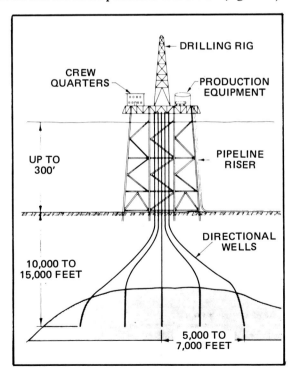

Figure 4.46. A drilling platform is often designed for directional drilling.

In order to accomplish this goal, the platform is constructed with drilling slots arranged in rows forming a rectangle. A movable drilling derrick is mounted on a grid somewhat resembling a checkerboard. Slots are spaced laterally to allow for the installation of the Christmas trees when the wells are completed. Multiple drilling slots are used by skidding the derrick from one drilling slot to the next. Of platforms currently under construction, most have twelve slots; the second most common is the twenty-four-slot platform.

Many platforms have derricks that can be used for two or more wells by skidding the crown block, the rotary, and drawworks. For severe weather locations, drilling slots provide access to the seafloor through the piles that support the platform.

Personnel safety

Periodic emergency drills are necessary for personnel safety on the offshore rig. Every occupant of the mobile rig or platform must be familiar with escape routes and alternate routes. Specific duties are assigned for hasty abandonment if systems are to be stopped from operating.

The rig may be equipped with a chute or slide from deck to water surface. A sufficient number of lifeboats or escape capsules must be available, and the proper methods of boarding and launching must be known by everyone. Some survival capsules are powered and provided with air supplies. Many structures have heliports for helicopters, which might be used for emergency evacuations. Specific instruction on the effective use of all safety equipment is standard procedure on offshore rigs.

WELL CONTROL

The Lucas gusher, which blew 700 feet of 4-inch drill pipe over 100 feet in the air and then sprayed 50,000 barrels of oil a day for nine days before the well could be controlled, was probably one of the most famous blowouts in history (fig. 4.47). It was 1901, and the drillers had never seen or heard of a blowout. Perhaps if they had, they would have recognized the signs of an impending eruption before it occurred.

The signs were all there: shows of oil and gas in the drilling fluid, a sudden increase in the drilling rate, increased flow of mud into the mud pits, kicks of drilling mud flowing from the well casing, and lightened drill stem weight.

The unmistakable signs of oil and gas in the mud were present before and after casing was set. This was encouraging to the drillers

Figure 4.47. The Lucas gusher at
Spindletop, near Beaumont, Texas,
sprayed 50,000 barrels of oil a day
for nine days in 1901 before the well
could be controlled.

who hoped the well would produce 50 barrels per day; they had no idea that a well could flow at a thousand times that rate. It had taken the contractor nearly three months to reach 880 feet, an average of about 10 feet of hole per day. After setting casing at that depth, the drilling rate stepped up to 20 feet daily, and everyone was elated with the fast progress. It is now known that drilling speed drastically improves when formation pressure and mud column pressure are nearly the same. The driller was able to make hole quickly because the well was about to blow out. The derrickman came down when the first heavy kicks showered the derrick with drilling mud. There was no weight indicator, but the hook load certainly lightened as the pipe began to come out of the well.

Oilwell blowouts are wasteful, not only of time and money spent for control, but of pressure in the formation, which is needed to move the oil from the underground reservoir up to the surface (fig. 4.48). No one was hurt by the blowout of the Lucas well, but men have been killed or injured by similar disasters. Although blowouts have caused losses of life and property, experienced crews can minimize the danger by taking the necessary precautions, recognizing the signs of a kick, and using their blowout prevention equipment properly.

Pressure

The key to well control is to keep the hydrostatic pressure of the mud column higher than the formation pressure. Hydrostatic pressure is pressure of a fluid that is standing still. (The term *hydrostatic* comes from the words *hydro*, which means water or liquid, and *static*, which means at rest.) Both the fluid in the formation and the drilling mud in the wellbore are under hydrostatic pressure; however, in well control the term *hydrostatic pressure* refers to the force exerted by the noncirculating drilling mud or fluid in the wellbore with the well shut in. The force exerted by the formation fluid outside the wellbore is called *formation pressure.*

Both formation pressure and hydrostatic pressure depend on the *true vertical depth* (TVD) at which these pressures are measured and the *density* (or weight) of each fluid at its point of measurement. Pressure gained with depth is called *pressure gradient*. Fresh water has a pressure gradient of 0.433 pounds per square inch (psi) per foot. Thus, a hole full of fresh water that is 10 feet deep exerts 4.33 psi at the bottom of the hole, one that is 100 feet deep exerts 43.3 psi on bottom, and so on. Denser fluids have higher gradients than lighter fluids. Salt water, for example, has a gradient of 0.465 and at 100 feet would exert a pressure of 46.5 psi. Mud with a weight of 10 pounds per gallon (ppg) has a pressure gradient of 0.52 psi per foot. With this information, the proper mud weight can be calculated and kept in or circulated through the hole to prevent formation fluids from entering the well. The weight used in most normal drilling situations is 10 ppg.

Figure 4.48. The aftermath of a blowout around 1932
(Courtesy of Humanities Research Center, The University of Texas at Austin)

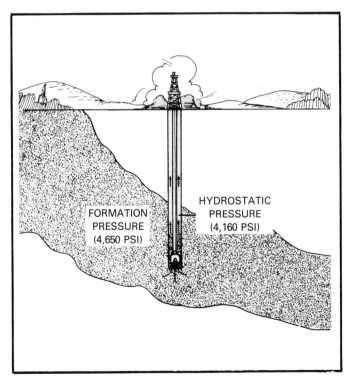

FORMATION PRESSURE (4,650 PSI)

HYDROSTATIC PRESSURE (4,160 PSI)

Fig. 4.49. A kick occurs when the formation pressure becomes greater than the hydrostatic or circulating pressure in the wellbore.

Kicks and their causes

A kick occurs when the pressure exerted by the drilling fluid in the wellbore becomes lower than the pressure exerted by the formation fluids, allowing a formation fluid—water, gas, or oil—to enter the wellbore (fig. 4.49). Put another way, when hydrostatic pressure is lower than formation pressure, fluids enter the wellbore (i.e., a kick occurs), and a blowout *may* occur if the crew does not take proper steps to control the well. A blowout is the uncontrolled spew of oil, salt water, burning gas, and/or other fluids from a wellbore into the atmosphere.

Understanding the causes and recognizing the warning signs of a kick are necessary for an effective well control program. The most common cause of a kick is the loss of wellbore pressure due to insufficient mud in the hole. A kick can also be caused by swabbing, lost circulation, and abnormally high formation pressure.

Insufficient mud in hole

A drop in the mud level in the wellbore happens when the drill stem is being pulled from the hole. Just as pulling a pencil out of a glass of water lowers the level of the water, so does the level of mud in the well drop when the drill stem is removed. The result is an immediate drop in the hydrostatic pressure in the wellbore, which could lead to a kick if mud is not put into the hole to replace the drill pipe.

Not only must the mud level in the wellbore be maintained, the mud must be of the correct density to have sufficient mud weight. This weight must counterbalance the formation pressure.

Swabbing

The swabbing, or sucking, action of the drill stem as it is being pulled from the hole can cause formation fluids to be drawn into the hole even if the hole is full of mud of the proper weight. If enough formation fluids are swabbed into the hole, the well can kick. So, it is important for the driller to know how much mud each stand of pipe displaces and to see that an equivalent amount of mud is actually put into the hole. If a discrepancy occurs—that is, if the hole requires less than the correct amount of mud to replace the amount of drill stem pulled, then it is quite likely that formation fluids have been swabbed into the hole. Once swabbing has been recognized, it is important to run the pipe back to bottom and circulate the intruded fluids out of the hole.

Lost circulation

Lost circulation is the loss of mud to a formation, evidenced by the complete or partial failure of the mud to return to the surface as it is circulated in the hole. For loss of circulation to occur, there must be formation openings to accept the mud and an excessive pressure to force it into the formation. Lost circulation can be caused by poor cement jobs, very coarse and permeable formations such as loose gravel, and fissured or fractured formations (fig. 4.50).

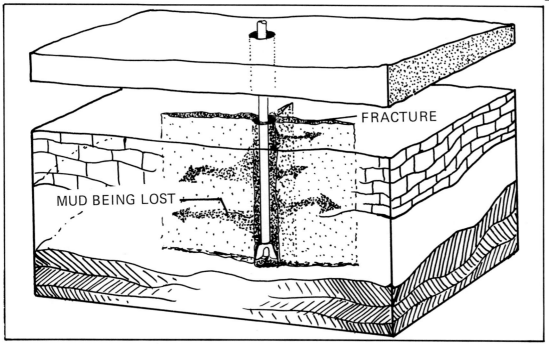

Figure 4.50. Mud is lost in fractured formations.

Drilling through an area of abnormally high formation pressure can cause the formation pressure to become greater than the hydrostatic pressure of the wellbore. The solution is to be able to recognize the signs of abnormal pressure and to increase the weight of the mud correspondingly.

Abnormal formation pressure

Blowout prevention equipment is designed to (1) close the top of the hole; (2) control the release of fluids; (3) permit pumping into the hole; and (4) allow movement of the drill pipe. The equipment must be capable of fast operation and allow the crew doing the job to be clear of any danger. A rig is generally equipped with a blowout preventer (BOP) stack, a choke manifold, choke and kill lines, and control panels. All units must be designed, built, and maintained to specifications that meet the requirements of the well operation in which they are installed. The BOP stack is attached to the well beneath the rig floor on a land rig and usually on a nonfloating offshore rig. On a floater, such as a drill ship or semisubmersible, a subsea blowout preventer stack is installed at the wellhead on the ocean floor.

Blowout prevention equipment

A BOP stack (fig. 4.51) consists of large, high-pressure valves that afford a means of shutting in a well at the surface when formation pressure exceeds pressure produced by the mud column. Two basic types of blowout preventers are ram and annular. Ram preventers use rams to seal off pressure on a hole. Rams can be blind, pipe, or

Figure 4.51. A blowout preventer stack is installed under the rig floor on a land rig or on a nonfloating offshore rig.

shear and may be installed on several preventers mounted in a stack on top of the wellbore. Blind rams, when closed, form a seal on a hole that has no drill pipe in it; pipe rams seal around pipe; and shear rams cut through drill pipe to form a seal. The annular preventer is installed above the ram preventers and forms a seal in the annular space between the pipe and wellbore or, if no pipe is present, on the wellbore itself.

A subsea BOP stack (fig. 4.52) is similar to a regular BOP but usually includes more preventers, valves, and fittings. A subsea BOP can be used on any type of offshore rig but is *necessary* on a floating rig. The continuous motion of a floater requires that wellheads and blowout preventers be installed on the ocean floor. This is made possible by the use of a marine riser system, which consists of special pipes and fittings, that guides the drill stem from the drilling vessel to the wellhead on the seafloor and conducts the drilling fluid from the well to the vessel. The system also has special devices, called motion compensators, to compensate for up and down movement of

Figure 4.52. A subsea blowout preventer stack is installed on the seafloor when a floating rig is used for drilling.

the drilling rig caused by the waves. The wellhead itself is designed to be compatible with these techniques and equipment.

The choke manifold, connected to the blowout preventer stack with a choke line, is an arrangement of pipes and chokes that controls the rate of flow as a kick is circulated out of the hole and drilling mud is circulated in (fig. 4.53). A choke is a special valve through which the drilling mud is circulated when the blowout preventers are closed. It may be fixed, adjustable, or automatic. Drilling fluid and gas passing through a choke go to a mud-gas separator, which saves usable mud and removes flammable gas to a safe distance from the rig.

A control panel, usually part of the driller's panel on the rig floor, opens and closes the valves and lines in the BOP stack. In addition, the BOP can generally be controlled from a remote panel situated off the rig floor (fig. 4.54).

Figure 4.53. The choke manifold has chokes and other devices that enable the driller to relieve downhole pressures without loss of control when the well is closed in by the blowout preventers.

Figure 4.54. A remote control station for blowout preventers

Formation pressure that is greater than the hydrostatic pressure in the hole will give advance evidence of its presence to an observant crew. Sometimes this evidence is obvious, such as a rapid flow from the well. At other times, it might be obscure and show up only as a very slow gain of fluid in the pit (pit gain). These indications may occur after a mechanical operation has been performed; for example, when the casing has been perforated or after a plug has been drilled out, the wellbore may be exposed to a formation pressure greater than can be controlled by the column of fluid in the wellbore.

Some of the preliminary events that may be found in association with kicks and blowouts are flow of mud from the well when the mud pump is shut off; pit gain; a show of salt water, oil, or gas; and gas-cut mud. Several events may occur in sequence: a flow of mud from the well; pit gain; and a show of gas, oil, or salt water before the well will really start to unload. A common occurrence, where drill pipe is raised too fast, is to experience a kick after the fluid level drops in the wellbore. In this instance, the usual events preliminary to a blowout may not take place. The blowout will be underway when the fluid hits the surface.

Indications of a blowout

When there are indications of a kick from the well, the first line of defense is usually to shut down the pumps and seal or close the blowout preventers. If the blowout preventers are closed, the drilling fluid or mud cannot escape out of the wellbore. The choke line, with a pressure gauge attached to it, is designed to allow the crew to circulate the intruded fluid out of the well while circulating in heavier mud to control the downhole pressure. The choke line allows gas, which is working its way to the surface from the bottom of the wellbore, to escape harmlessly into the atmosphere. But, if the choke does not allow pressure to escape fast enough, the formation itself will give way from too much pressure inside the wellbore. This kind of blowout can be very expensive and can ruin the hole for further drilling. Sometimes loss of circulation can be overcome by circulating the coarsest possible sealing materials to seal the formation leak and thereby killing the well. If the formation is fractured above the zone of production, then the formation pressure in the producing zone is not destroyed, and the driller can try to salvage the well by pumping heavy mud between the bottom of the wellbore and the point of circulation loss. But if the formation is fractured below the producing zone, then the driller has to kill the well by sealing the loss first, then controlling the pressure.

Killing a threatened blowout

Subsequent pressure buildup may be too high to permit leaving the preventers closed, but this cannot be determined without at least a temporary shut-in. Pressure limitations of the casing and wellhead equipment must be predetermined. These must be adhered to, not only at the time of the shut-in, but at any time while circulating out a kick. Closing in the well can, in some few cases, be dangerous—for example, with a short string of surface casing set—as it may result in a blowout around the casing.

SPECIAL DRILLING PROCEDURES

Fishing

Fishing is the industry's term for retrieving any item—or *fish*—from the wellbore. The fish can be anything from part or all of the drill stem stuck in the hole to smaller pieces of equipment such as a bit cone, a hand tool, or any nondrillable item in the hole. Occasionally, even iron pyrite may block the hole and must be removed.

**Freeing
stuck pipe**

Drill pipe gets stuck in the hole for several reasons: the hole can collapse around the pipe; the pipe can get stuck in a *key seat,* or *dogleg;* or pressure differential can hold the pipe securely to the wall of the hole.

The most common reason for the wall collapsing around the pipe is that the interstitial salt water, which is present in the pores of all formations, forms a bond with the water in the drilling mud. If the formation happens to be made of shale and the water in the drilling mud is in contact with the water in the shale, the water in the mud has a tendency to transfer to the shale. This can cause the shale to expand; then small sheets of shale slough off into the hole, the hole eventually fills with debris, and the pipe sticks.

Pipe can also get stuck in the hole when the formation pressure and the pressure within the wellbore differ too much. When drilling through permeable layers of the formation without adjusting the properties of the drilling mud to compensate for such formations, the higher pressure in the wellbore can cause a fairly thick cake of solid mud to build up on the inside wall of the hole. This wall cake may exert enough force against the drill collars to make them stick during tripping out.

To free the pipe from shale or wall cake, a device called a *free-point indicator* is lowered down through the drill pipe, like dangling a fishing line down a well (fig. 4.55). The device locates the stuck joint, and then another instrument called a *string shot* is lowered to the stuck point on the indicator line. The string shot is a long, thin stringlike explosive charge that is usually positioned at a tool joint several joints of pipe above the point where the pipe is stuck. As the charge is fired, the driller backs out, or removes, all of the joints above the stuck one. The stuck pipe is left dangling in the hole, and a special kind of pipe called *washover pipe,* which is larger in diameter than the

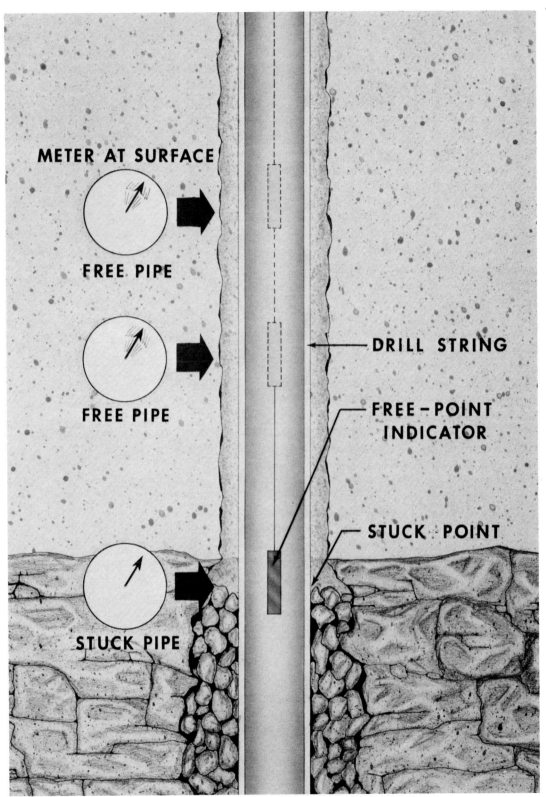

METER AT SURFACE

FREE PIPE

FREE PIPE

STUCK PIPE

DRILL STRING

FREE-POINT INDICATOR

STUCK POINT

Figure 4.55. A free-point indicator is used to locate stuck pipe.

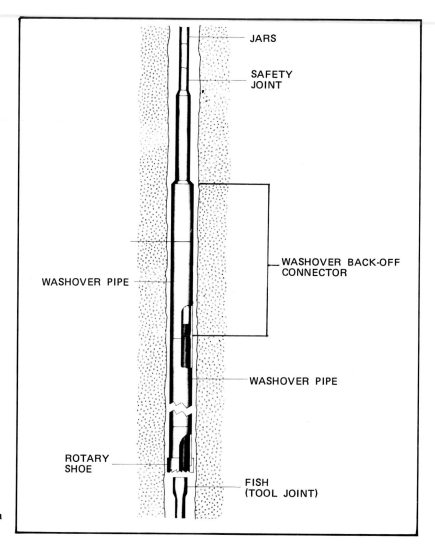

JARS

SAFETY
JOINT

WASHOVER BACK-OFF
CONNECTOR

WASHOVER PIPE

WASHOVER PIPE

ROTARY
SHOE

FISH
(TOOL JOINT)

Figure 4.56. A washover string with back-off connector tool

stuck drill pipe, is run into the hole. The washover pipe has a *rotary shoe* that grinds up the shale or wall cake that is causing the pipe to stick (fig. 4.56). However, if all the wall cake holding the drill pipe is removed, the drill pipe will fall to the bottom. To prevent this, a *back-off connector* is attached to the top of the stuck pipe inside the washover pipe. This device rotates separately from the washover pipe and is shaped so that it will screw into the top of the stuck tool joint. After all the shale and wall cake are ground up, the washover pipe and the drill pipe (secured inside the washover pipe) are pulled up simultaneously.

If the pipe gets stuck in a dogleg, or key seat, it is probably because the drilling angle deviated slightly in the process of making hole. Then, when the drill stem is pulled from the hole, the pipe or the slightly wider drill collars stick at the dogleg. Since the borehole of a well is seldom a straight line, the opportunity for doglegs and stuck pipe is always present.

If the drill stem is stuck at a dogleg, the fishing process is slightly different (fig. 4.57); however, it starts with sending the free-point indicator and string shot down the hole as before. When the stuck point is located, all but the last five or six joints above the stuck drill collar are removed, so that the top of the pipe section is in the main borehole and not in the dogleg area. Then a device called a *bumper jar* is lowered down the hole, made up on the fish, and dropped heavily on the stuck fish, bumping or jarring the pipe loose (fig. 4.58). Usually, a reaming device called a key-seat wiper is run in with the jar so that the key seat can be reamed out to a larger size. This way the drill collars will pass through the enlarged key seat.

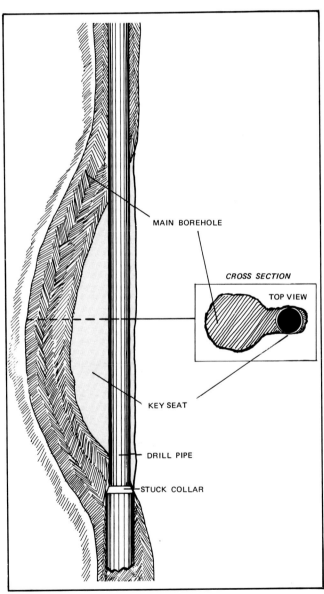

Figure 4.57. Drill collar stuck in key seat

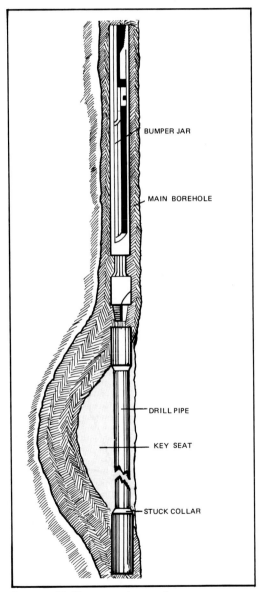

Figure 4.58. Key-seat wiper and bumper jar

128

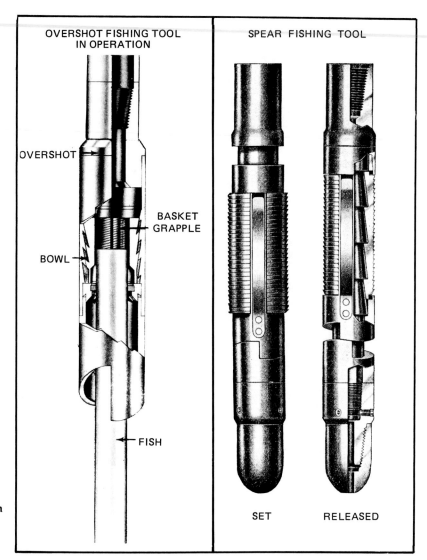

OVERSHOT FISHING TOOL
IN OPERATION

OVERSHOT

BOWL

BASKET
GRAPPLE

← FISH

SPEAR FISHING TOOL

SET   RELEASED

Figure 4.59. An overshot, shown in operation at left, and the spear are two commonly used tools for retrieving fish.

Two commonly used tools for retrieving fish are the *overshot* and the *spear* (fig. 4.59). An overshot or spear is run into the hole and attached to the fish, then both the tool and the fish are pulled out of the hole together. An overshot grips the outside of the fish, while a spear attaches to the inside. Special mills are sometimes used to grind the top of the fish, making it easier to attach the overshot or spear.

Retrieving junk

Small nondrillable pieces that find their way into the bottom of the hole and cause drilling to cease are known as *junk*. Many fishing tools including powerful magnets and special baskets through which mud can be circulated, are used to retrieve junk. In fact, the only limit to fishing tools and methods seems to be the imagination and ingenuity of the people faced with the problem of removing fish from the hole.

Although wellbores are normally planned to be drilled vertically, many occasions arise that make it necessary or advantageous to drill at an angle, especially in offshore operations. This deviation from drilling a straight hole, known as controlled directional drilling, makes it possible to drill as many as twenty or more wells using the same rig.

Directional drilling is used most commonly on offshore wells. Because the erection of a single platform may cost a million dollars or more, to erect one for each well might not be profitable. By using directional drilling, several wellbores can be started from a single platform and then deviated, so that the wells bottom out in the production zone.

Directional drilling has other applications (fig. 4.60). Wells may be drilled from the shoreline and deflected to reach a pay zone offshore. It is used for exploratory drilling to find the exact location of a fault plane. When it is impossible to locate the drilling rig over the desired spot because of a river, hill, or some other obstruction, it can be erected to one side and the hole deviated to the pay zone. Directional drilling is also used to bypass some of the problems that occur downhole and in the vicinity of salt domes. Another use is in killing a blowout. A relief well or offset well is drilled and deviated so that it bottoms out near the borehole of the blowout well. Then mud under high pressure is pumped down the offset well and channeled to control the blowout.

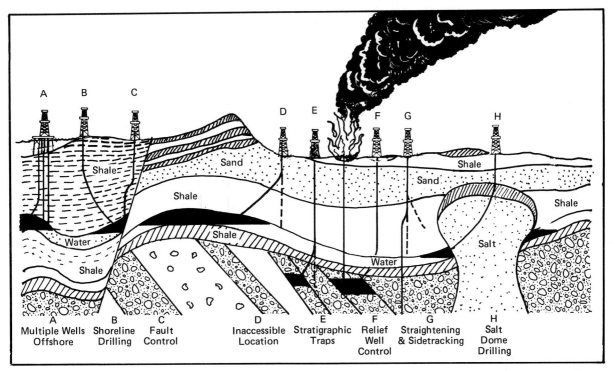

Figure 4.60. The applications of controlled directional drilling are many.

Special tools and techniques are required for directional drilling. To deviate the hole from vertical, a bent sub (short for substitute) and a downhole motor are used. A bent sub is a short cylindrical piece of pipe that is threaded on both ends and bent in the middle. It is installed in the drill stem between the bottommost drill collar and a downhole motor. A downhole motor, driven by drilling fluid, imparts rotary motion only to the drilling bit connected to the tool, thus eliminating the need to turn the entire drill stem in order to make hole. Shaped like a piece of pipe, a downhole motor can have turbine blades or it can be a multicurved steel shaft that turns inside an eliptically shaped opening in a housing. The downhole motor is made up between the bent sub and the bit.

To orient the drilling in the desired direction, various types of compasses, directional gyroscopes, and photographic or electronic readout devices are used. Because of the bent sub, the hole starts at an angle of from 1 to 3 degrees, and the angle increases as drilling progresses. Periodically, the hole is surveyed or checked for direction and angle of deflection.

Deviation tools and instruments are usually rented from a service company. Also, the company's directional drilling engineer supervises the operation and assumes responsibility for the company's tools and instruments.

Air drilling

Circulating with air instead of mud is an alternate method of drilling that has spectacular results but is used only in special cases. Penetration rates are higher, footage per bit is greater, and bit cost is lower with air. Air cleans the bottom of the hole more effectively than mud, air expansion at the bit is very efficient for cooling, and cuttings are transported quickly to the surface. Even though the cuttings are very small, identification of the formation drilled can be made when using air, and indications of gas, oil, or water can be detected very rapidly.

However, air drilling has several negative aspects that are considered more significant than the positive ones. The hazard of fire or explosion is always present. Because air does not impose much pressure at the bottom of the hole, there can be no high-pressure formations encountered in drilling. It is impossible to prevent the entry of formation fluids into the well, and most deep wells encounter water-bearing formations sooner or later. If the walls of the well tend to slough, or cave, into the hole, air circulation is impossible because the drill stem may stick. Also, corrosion to the drill stem has been a problem with air drilling, although chemicals have been developed to take care of this problem.

To drill with air, large compressors and related equipment are moved onto the site. Usually, only part of a hole will be drilled with air, then the rig will be changed over to drilling mud. Actually, air is not circulated in the sense that it is used over and over again; rather, it makes one trip from the compressors, down the drill stem, out the bit, and up the annulus back to the surface, where it is blown out a blooey line, or vent pipe (fig. 4.61).

Figure 4.61. Skid-mounted compressors furnish the high-pressure air used on this regular rotary rig for drilling. The air can be seen blowing a cloud of dust out of the blooey line in the foreground.

Aerated mud—that is, mud to which air has been purposely added—has been used successfully to stop lost circulation. Lost circulation occurs when drilling mud leaks out of the borehole and into a subsurface formation. Thus, the mud does not return to the surface but is lost downhole. The air in the mud reduces the amount of pressure exerted by the mud on downhole formations and thus relieves one of the causes of lost circulation.

Production

in the petroleum industry, production is defined as the phase of operation that deals with bringing the well fluids to the surface and preparing them for their trip through the pipeline to the refinery. Since this phase begins after the well is drilled, the first step is to complete the well—that is, to perform whatever operations are necessary to start the well fluids flowing to the surface. Routine maintenance operations, such as replacing worn or malfunctioning equipment, are standard during the well's producing life, and more extensive repairs—known as workovers—may also be necessary to maintain the flow of oil and gas. Because well fluids are usually a mixture of oil, gas, and water, the fluid must be separated into its components. These must be treated, measured, and tested before they are run to the pipeline on their way to the refinery. Thus, it can be seen that production is a combination of operations: bringing the fluids to the surface; doing whatever is necessary to keep the well producing; and taking the fluids through a series of steps to purify, test, and measure them.

WELL COMPLETION

After a well has been drilled to the projected depth and the productive formations have been evaluated for their economic worth and profit, work will begin to set the casing, prepare the well for production, and bring in the zone or zones. Completion equipment and the methods employed are quite varied, and the decisions for an individual well are usually based on the type of oil or gas accumulations involved, the requirements that may develop during the life of the well, and the economic circumstances at the time when the work is done. Low-pressure, sometimes secondhand, pipe will be employed if the oil accumulation has a marginal payout, and other expenditures will be scaled down accordingly. If high pressure is anticipated and well life is expected to be long, however, the best grade of pipe with backup precautions will be needed.

The well

Typically, an oil or gas well will require three concentric strings of large pipe: conductor pipe, surface casing, and oil string casing. The conductor pipe prevents the hole from caving in at the surface and endangering the drilling rig foundation. It is usually cemented, but occasionally it is driven into place by a pile driver. When the surface casing is set and cemented in place, it provides protection for freshwater formations (fig. 5.1). It also prevents loose shale and sand

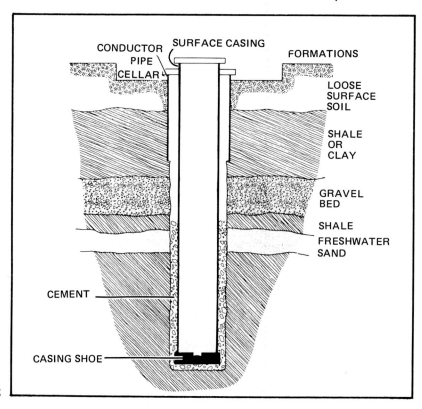

Figure 5.1. Surface casing

or gravel from falling into the hole and affords a means for controlling the flow of fluid from the well. Setting depths may vary from 500 feet to 5,000 feet. The final casing for most wells is the oil string, or long string (fig. 5.2). The producing formation is usually completely cased off, but sometimes the oil string is set near or just on top of the potential pay zone.

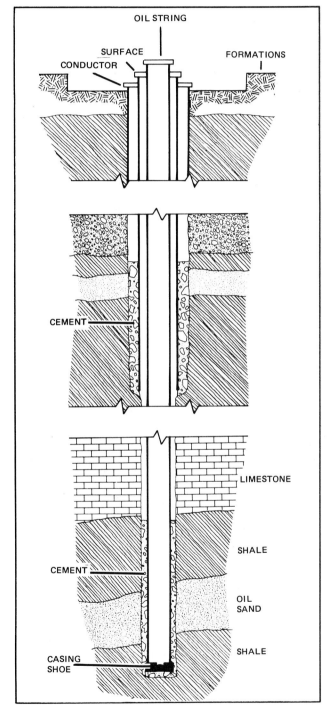

Figure 5.2. Oil string casing

The final string of pipe usually run in a producing well is the tubing (fig. 5.3). Tubing is nearly always freely suspended in the well from the casinghead. Its small diameter produces more efficient results than casing in a flowing well. Tubing also makes a safer well completion possible. Another advantage is that tubing is comparatively easy to remove when it becomes plugged or damaged. Tubing, in conjunction with a packer, keeps well fluids away from the casing because the packer seals the space between the tubing and casing.

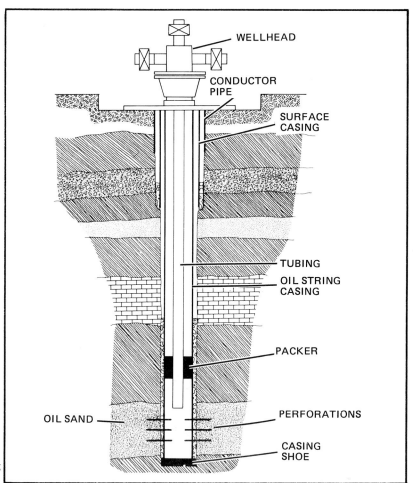

Figure 5.3. Casing, tubing, and packer arrangement in a flowing well

The wellhead

The wellhead is the equipment used to maintain surface control of the well. It forms a seal to prevent well fluids from blowing or leaking at the surface. The conditions expected to be encountered in the individual well determine the type of wellhead that is needed. Sometimes, all that is required is a simple assembly to support the weight of the tubing in the well. In other cases, the control of formation pressures is necessary, and a high-pressure wellhead is required. Pressures greater than 20,000 pounds per square inch have been found in some fields.

The wellhead is made up of a combination of parts called the casinghead, tubing head, Christmas tree, stuffing box, and pressure gauges.

The casinghead is a heavy steel fitting at the surface to which the casing is attached. It provides a housing for the equipment from which intermediate strings of casing are suspended. During drilling and workover operations, the casinghead is used as an anchor for the pressure control equipment that may be necessary.

Casinghead

Similar in design and use to the casinghead, the tubing head supports the tubing string, seals off pressures between the casing and the inside of tubing, and provides connections at the surface with which the flowing liquid or gas can be controlled. The tubing head is supported by the casinghead if a casinghead is used on the well.

Tubing head

The control valves, pressure gauges, and chokes assembled at the top of a well to control the flow of oil and gas after the well has been drilled and completed are known as the Christmas tree, so named because of its shape and the large number of fittings branching out above the wellhead (fig. 5.4). The pressure gauges reveal casing and tubing pressures. By knowing these pressures under various operating conditions, better well control is possible.

Christmas tree

Figure 5.4. Christmas tree

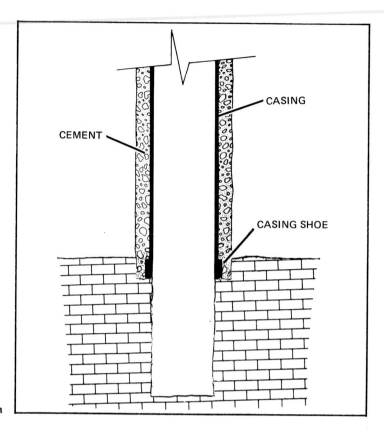

Figure 5.5. Open-hole completion

Completion methods

A well servicing contractor may move in a smaller rig to perform the operations necessary to put the well into production. The type of completion method used is determined by the characteristics of the reservoir and its economic potential. Among the various methods are open-hole, liner, and perforated casing completions.

Open-hole completion

An open-hole, or barefoot, completion has no production casing or liner set opposite the producing formation (fig. 5.5). Reservoir fluids flow unrestricted into the open wellbore. This type of completion, used rarely and generally restricted to limestone reservoirs, is useful where only one productive zone and low-pressure formations exist. In an open-hole completion, casing is set just above the pay zone, and drilling or coring proceeds into the productive zone as far as necessary to complete the well.

Liner completion

In the liner completion method, a specially equipped pipe known as a *liner* is set opposite the producing interval to hold up sloughing shale or to prevent sand from entering the wellbore. Various types of liners are used, although a common method is to set and cement blank pipe in place and perforate it. Special equipment is used to wash the liner to the bottom of the well, cement it, and seal the space between the liner and the casing with a packer.

The perforated casing completion—by far the most popular method of completing a well—requires a good primary cementing job and the proper perforating method. Perforating is the process of piercing the casing wall and the cement to provide holes through which formation fluids may enter the wellbore. The perforating method used should penetrate the producing formation as far as possible, shoot a smooth and round entrance hole in the casing with the least amount of damage, and produce the maximum flow rate with a minimum number of holes.

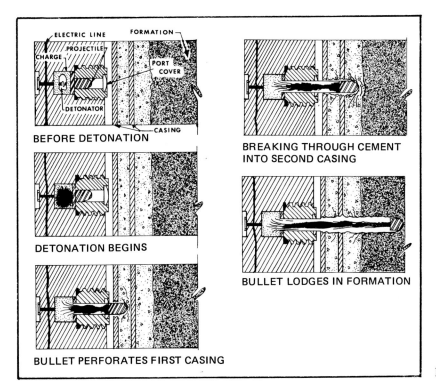

Figure 5.6. Bullet perforation

A safer well completion technique is to make the perforations after the tubing has been run and the packer set because the well is under absolute control at all times. Thru-tubing perforation has been made possible by the development of perforating devices small enough to run through tubing.

Two basic methods of perforating are *bullet perforating* and *jet perforating*. Bullet perforators are lowered into the hole and fired electrically from the surface (fig. 5.6). Bullets produce a round, uniform, large, smooth entrance hole, and they characteristically cause hairline cracks, or fractures, at the end of the perforation. In jet perforating, shaped-charge explosives are used instead of buttlets (fig. 5.7). Shaped charges product maximum penetration in hard rock and is more widely used than bullet perforating.

140

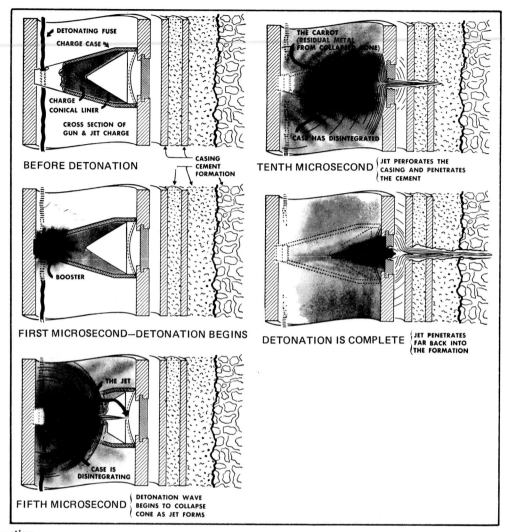

Figure 5.7. Jet perforation

Swabbing

A temporary operation that lowers the fluid level in the well so that it can begin to produce is known as swabbing. If enough fluid can be swabbed, or lifted, out of the tubing so that the pressure in the formation is slightly greater than the hydrostatic pressure of the fluid in the tubing, the oil or gas will start flowing immediately after the perforations are made. If the well does not flow after being swabbed, a pump is installed as a permanent lifting device to bring the oil to the surface.

Well testing

Well tests are conducted to determine production rates for oil and gas wells. There are a variety of well tests, and each reveals certain information about a particular well and the reservoir in which it is completed. Accuracy is, of course, very important, and these test data form the case history of a well.

The potential test is a measurement of the largest amount of oil and gas that a well will produce in a 24-hour period under certain fixed conditions. This test is made on each newly completed well and at other times during the well's producing life. Potential test information is generally required by the state regulatory group, which uses it to establish the producing allowable for the well.

Potential test

A bottomhole pressure test measures the reservoir pressure of the well at a point opposite the producing formation. The test is usually conducted after the well has been shut in for 24 to 48 hours. When this test is conducted at scheduled intervals, valuable information about the decline or depletion of the zone in which the well is producing will be gathered.

Bottomhole pressure test

A productivity test is conducted to determine the effects of different flow rates on the pressure within the producing zone of the well. This reveals certain physical characteristics of the reservoir, and the maximum potential rate of flow can be calculated without risking the damage that might occur if the well were produced at its maximum possible flow rate. The procedure for the test is first to measure the closed-in bottomhole pressure of the well and then to measure the flowing bottomhole pressure at several stabilized rates of flow. This type of testing is done on both oil and gas wells and is the most widely accepted method of determining the capacity of gas wells. In many states, the regulation of gas production is based upon a test of this type.

Productivity test

WELL SERVICING AND WORKOVER

Well servicing is the maintenance work performed on an oil or gas well to improve or maintain the production from a formation already producing. A well servicing unit carries the hoisting machinery that is used to pull sucker rods, an operation that is done most frequently for pump changes or rod string repairs (fig. 5.8). The same unit can be used to pull tubing by arranging the equipment for the heavier load. The most common well servicing operations are those related to artificial lift installations, tubing string repairs, and work on other downhole equipment that may be malfunctioning.

Like well servicing, the purpose of a workover is to increase production of a producing well, but workovers include more extensive repairs. Workover rigs, in many respects, are scaled down drilling rigs (fig. 5.9). They are equipped to stand the pipe in the derrick, they have some arrangement for turning the pipe string while it is in the hole, and they are furnished with a high-pressure pump. The pump is used to circulate fluid in the well—that is, to force water or other liquid inside the tubing to the bottom of the well by pump pressure and then outside the tubing back to the surface into

Figure 5.8. Truck mounted well
servicing unit

Figure 5.9. Self-propelled workover rig

a tank to complete the circuit. A workover includes any work ✗ performed to change the producing zone in a well, to clean out, or to reach an old producing interval.

When a well is first completed, the fluid is expected to flow to the surface by natural reservoir energy for some period of time. At some time during their economic life, however, most oilwells will require some form of artificial lift to help raise the fluid to the surface and obtain the maximum recovery of oil for maximum profit to the producer. The most common methods of artificial lift are gas lift, sucker rod pumps, hydraulic pumps, and submersible pumps.

Artificial lift
(4)

If a supply of gas is economically available and the amount of fluid will justify the expense, gas lift is commonly used (fig. 5.10). In the gas lift process, gas is injected into the fluid column of a well to lighten and raise the fluid by expansion of the gas. Injected gas aerates the fluid to make it exert less pressure than the formation does; consequently, the high formation pressure forces the fluid out of the wellbore. Gas may be injected continuously or intermittently, depending on the producing characteristics of the well and the arrangement of the gas lift equipment.

Gas lift ✗

144

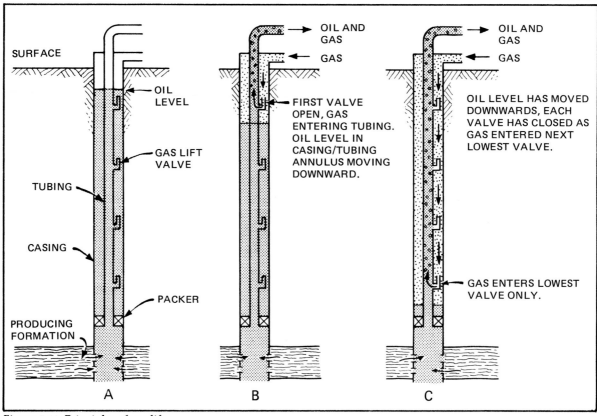

Figure 5.10. Principles of gas lift

⚹ *Sucker rod pumps*

The artificial lift method that involves sucker rod pumps is commonly known as rod pumping, or beam pumping. Surface equipment used in this method imparts an up-and-down motion to a sucker rod string that is attached to a piston, or plunger, pump submerged in the fluid of a well. Most rod pumping units have the same general operating principles (fig. 5.11).

⚹ *Hydraulic pumps*

Hydraulic pumps are so called because they are operated by a hydraulic motor in the unit at the bottom of the well. The fluid used to drive the motor is the oil from the well itself. The motor, in turn, drives a pump that pumps the oil to the surface.

One type of hydraulic pump is the free pump. This pump is installed in the bottom of the tubing and is operated by oil taken from a tank at the surface and pumped downward through the tubing. The power oil is returned to the surface through the small tubing, along with new oil taken from the formation. Other types of hydraulic pumps are available, and all of them use the same basic fluid motor and pump in the bottom of the hole. The motor and pumping unit are lowered into the well on a string of tubing, and the pump and power-oil tubing can be run either inside the regular well tubing or inside the casing.

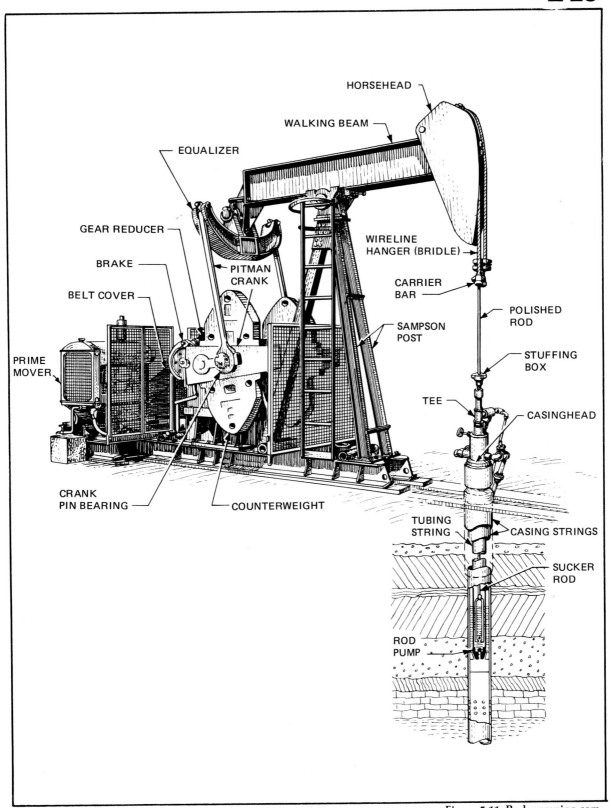

Figure 5.11. Rod pumping components

Submersible pumps

In many fields, older wells produce a large volume of water in relation to the volume of oil, and in order to be economically justifiable, tremendous volumes of fluid have to be lifted from the well. In these circumstances, an electric submersible pump may be installed either in the tubing or in the casing. Since both the pump motor and the pump are submerged in the well fluid, the electric current is supplied through a special heavy-duty armored cable.

Routine maintenance work

Routine maintenance work is needed throughout a well's life if economical production is to be maintained. Pump parts wear out and must be replaced periodically, rods break and must be repaired, and gas-lift devices must be replaced occasionally. Other remedial work needed to keep a well on steady production may include repair of tubing leaks, replacement of packers that have failed, and sand control.

Part replacement

Well equipment such as downhole pumps, sucker rods, gas lift valves, tubing, packers, and so forth must be in good working condition. Rod pumps ultimately wear out because of abrasive or corrosive conditions and their reciprocating characteristic. Sucker rods are often highly stressed and may ultimately fail because of repeated load reversals. Corrosion, scale, and paraffin deposits may accelerate such failures (fig. 5.12). Tubing—and rods for that matter—will wear due to the reciprocating movement in the well as the string stretches and unstretches to adjust to the changing fluid loads while pumping. Packers and other accessory devices sometimes fail because of the hydraulic and mechanical loads that are imposed on them.

Cleanout and sand control

Major cleanout and workover operations include sand removal, liner removal, casing repair, cementing, drilling deeper, or sidetracking. These jobs usually require a string of pipe that can be rotated. Also, it is generally necessary to circulate the well—that is, pump fluid to the bottom and back to the surface. Usually salt water or specially prepared circulating, or workover, fluid is used. Circulating the well (1) removes sand, cuttings, or chips; (2) prevents blowout by maintaining adequate hydrostatic pressure to overcome formation pressure; (3) cools bits and cutters; (4) actuates hydraulic tools; and (5) where open hole is involved, supports the wall of the hole until casing or liner can be set. These functions require a suitable circulating system, a pump, hose and swivel, string of pipe to bottom, and a pit or tank to receive fluid returning from the well.

Production men have tried for a hundred years to devise a method of keeping sand out of a well. Men who work in hard-rock country may never have sand trouble, but in California and the Gulf Coast

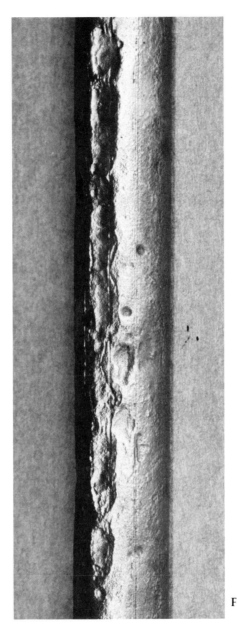

Figure 5.12. Corroded sucker rods

sand problems occur every day and are handled almost routinely. Loose sand is controlled by plastic squeeze, gravel pack, a screen liner, or a combination of these methods. Plastic squeeze involves placing a resinous material into the sand formation and then allowing the plastic to harden. In the gravel-packing process, graded gravel is placed outside the casing or liner; this gravel holds back the sand but allows the well fluids to enter the wellbore. One type of liner used to control sand is a slotted pipe with the slots cut transversely. The liner also acts to admit oil to the bottom of the well and exclude sand. When production shows sand, it usually indicates that the liner has failed and that remedial work is in order.

✗ Well stimulation

The term *well stimulation* encompasses several processes used to enlarge old channels or to create new ones in the producing formation. Since oil usually occurs in the pores or cracks of sand or limestone formations—and seldom, if ever, in an underground pool like a tank—enlarging or creating new channels means that the oil or gas will move more readily to a well. Three well stimulation methods have been developed: explosives, acid treatment, and hydraulic fracturing.

✗ Explosives

Using high explosives to improve a well's productive capacity began in the late 1800s and continued until acid treatment and hydraulic fracturing were developed in the 1940s. There has been, however, a revival of interest in explosive fracturing in recent years for the following reasons: (1) Certain kinds of tight formations do not respond readily to either acidizing or hydraulic fracturing. (2) Experience has shown that many of the older wells that were shot are still producing commercially, while wells that were hydraulically fractured or acidized are not. (3) Modern techniques and explosive materials have been developed to do a better and safer job than heretofore possible.

There are now two basic ways of using explosives for formation stimulation. The first is to concentrate detonation only in the borehole. The second is to inject the explosive away from the wellbore for dispersed detonation within a fracture system. Explosive fracturing supposedly enlarges the effective wellbore, eliminates nearby formation plugging, and at the instant of the explosion furnishes a source of high-pressure gas to force fluid into the formation at injection rates equivalent to 20 tons of water per second. The formation of rubble that is said to be produced by explosives should prevent fracture healing, making the use of proppants unnecessary.

✗ Acid treatment

Well servicing rigs are frequently called in to prepare both new and old wells for acid treatment. The primary purpose of this type of well stimulation is to dissolve rock, thus enlarging existing channels and opening new ones to the wellbore (fig. 5.13). Oil field acids must create reaction products that are soluble; otherwise, solid materials would be precipitated and plug the pore space in the rocks. The acid must also be relatively safe to handle, and, since large volumes are used, it must be fairly inexpensive. Reservoir rocks most commonly acidized are limestone (calcium carbonate) and dolomite, which is a mixture of calcium and magnesium carbonates.

Additives are used with oil field acids for many reasons, but the most important is to prevent or delay corrosion—that is, to inhibit the acid from attacking the steel tubing or casing in the well. A

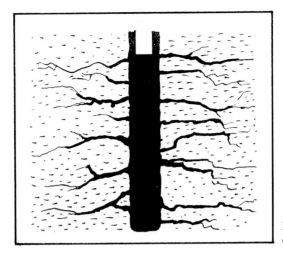

Figure 5.13. Acid enlarges existing channels or makes new ones.

surfactant, or surface active agent, is another type of additive. It is mixed in small amounts with an acid to make it easier to pump the mixture into the rock formation and to prevent spent acid and oil from forming emulsions. Other types of additives are sequestering agents and suspending agents.

Most limestone and dolomite formations have low permeabilities. Acid injection into these low-permeability formations, even at moderate rates, usually results in a fracture type of acid treatment, meaning that the pressure is high enough to cause the formation to crack. This is the most widely used treatment for well stimulation with acid. Another type of treatment—interstitial, or matrix, acidizing—also results in production increases. Interstitial acidizing consists of treating at a rate and pressure low enough to avoid fracturing the formation. This technique is usually used when formation damage is present or when a water zone or gas cap is nearby and fracturing might result in high water or excessive gas production.

Hydraulic fracturing

In recent years, formation fracturing by hydraulic pressure has gained wide acceptance. Since hydraulic fracturing does for sandstone reservoirs what acid treatment does for limestone or dolomite reservoirs, this type of stimulation may result in commercial production in an area where it was not feasible before.

Essentially, the process consists of applying hydraulic pressure against the formation by pumping fluid into the well (fig. 5.14). This pressure actually splits the rocks. Hydraulic fracturing is used to accomplish four basic jobs: (1) create penetrating reservoir fractures to improve the productivity of a well, (2) improve the ultimate recovery from a well by extending the flow channels farther into the

Figure 5.14. Equipment for a high-volume fracture treatment job, 1970

formations, (3) aid in secondary recovery operations, and (4) increase the rate of injection of brine and industrial waste material into disposal wells. Most wells are fractured on initial completion, and refracturing to restore productivity of a well is a regular procedure. Extension of the existing fractures will usually improve well productivity.

During early experimental work, it was discovered that a hydraulically formed fracture tends to heal, or lose its fluid-carrying capacity, after the parting pressure is released unless the fracture is propped open in some manner. This is the function of propping agents or proppants—to hold the fractures open. Sand, nutshells, and beads of aluminum, glass, and plastic may be used as propping agents. Spacer materials are used between the particles of the proppant to ensure its optimum distribution.

The fracturing fluid must not only break down the formation, but it must also extend and transport the propping agent into the fracture. The oil-base, water-base, or acid-base fracturing fluid and the additives used to modify its properties, along with the proppant and spacer, make up a very complex substance. Choice of the most suitable base depends on the chemical nature of the rock, its physical characteristics, and the nature of the reservoir fluid.

Fluid injection

Fluid injection is primarily a secondary recovery operation in which an essentially depleted reservoir is restored to producing status by the injection of liquids or gases (from extraneous sources) into the wellbore. In essence, this injection restores reservoir energy, moving the formerly unrecoverable secondary reserves through the reservoir to the well. This practice has become increasingly important in the oil industry as the demand for petroleum products continues to grow. Injection fluids of controlled composition are put into selected wells at or near discovery pressure to achieve maximum recovery efficiency. Some of the more common fluid-injection methods include waterflood, saltwater disposal, high-pressure gas drive, enriched gas drive, miscible flooding, and thermal processes.

Waterflood

Waterflood is a secondary recovery method that involves the injection of water through wells specially set up for water injection and the removal of the water and oil from the wells drilled adjacent to the injection wells. Although water for injection may be supplied from water-supply wells drilled specifically for this purpose, the water that is produced along with the oil may also be used.

Regardless of whether the water is injected into formations for disposal, pressure maintenance, or waterflood, the fluid must meet certain requirements. The injected water must be clear, stable, and similar to the water in the formation where it is being injected. It also must not be severely corrosive and must be free of materials that may plug the formation. If the water is severely corrosive, it may be treated with inhibitors or other chemicals to render it less corrosive, or corrosion-resistant materials may be used in the disposal equipment and wells. De-aerating, softening, filtering, chemical treating, stabilizing, and testing are common water-treatment processes.

Saltwater disposal

Although not a secondary recovery process, saltwater disposal is a common form of fluid injection. Its purpose is quite simply to dispose of the salt water produced with crude oil. A typical system is composed of collection centers in which salt water from several wells is gathered, a central treating plant in which salt water is conditioned to remove scale- or corrosion-forming substances, and a disposal well in which treated salt water is injected into a suitable formation.

The idea that water in a formation has reached a condition of chemical balance is the basis of the closed system of saltwater disposal. In this system, water can be transferred from one formation to another without plugging the second formation if the composition and properties of the water in both formations are reasonably similar and the chemical balance of the water is not changed.

High-pressure
gas drive

High-pressure gas drive is a secondary recovery method in which natural gas at high pressures—above 3,000 pounds per square inch—is injected into the reservoir (fig. 5.15). The gas mixes with the reservoir oil, forming a solvent zone, which results in almost complete displacement of the reservoir oil in that part of the formation.

Figure 5.15. High pressure gas drive

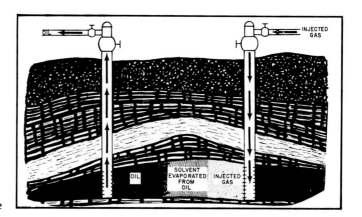

Figure 5.16. Enriched gas drive

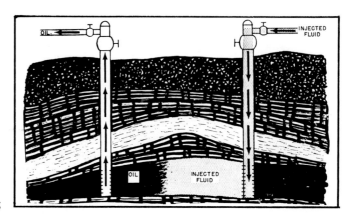

Figure 5.17. Miscible flooding

Enriched gas drive is similar to high-pressure gas drive in that they are both secondary-recovery methods. The main difference is that the gas to be injected is enriched with propane and butane (fig. 5.16). As this enriched gas contacts the reservoir oil, some of its elements condense into a solvent, swell the oil, reduce its viscosity, and change its flow properties. The swollen oil mixes with the injected gas and then moves toward the producing well.

Enriched gas drive

In miscible flooding, a solvent that is capable of being mixed with the reservoir oil is injected; then, a displacing fluid is injected to mix with the solvent (fig. 5.17). The injected displacing fluid moves the solvent through the reservoir while the solvent removes the oil from the portion of the reservoir through which it passes. Propane and butane are usually used as the solvents in this type of fluid injection, and the displacing fluid is generally natural gas. This gas is generally at a high enough pressure so that both the solvent mixture and the displacing fluid become liquid.

Miscible flooding

Heated water or steam may be injected to act as a displacement mechanism or to stimulate production from individual wells. The heat of the fluids lowers the viscosity of the oil in the reservoir and also provides reservoir drive. Although not involving fluid injection, another thermal process actually calls for burning some of the oil in a reservoir. Although this process appears to be wasteful, it actually uses some of the oil that could not be produced by any known method of recovery as an energy source to increase the total amount of oil recovered from the particular reservoir.

Thermal processes

SEPARATING AND TREATING WELL FLUIDS

Well fluids are often a complex mixture of oil, gas, and water, and they must be separated into their components and treated. This is a difficult job, and vapor recovery, evaporation control, and fire hazard elimination are some of the major considerations during this phase of production.

The simplest type of equipment used to separate the liquids from the gases is a tank in which the force of gravity is used to achieve the separation. Oil, which is heavier than gas, falls to the bottom of the

Separating equipment

tank and is then removed for additional treatment or sent to the storage tanks. The lighter element, gas, is removed from the top of the tank and enters the gas gathering system. Vertical and horizontal separators, which are more modern pieces of equipment, use forces in addition to gravity to achieve the best possible separation of well fluids.

Vertical separators

Well fluids enter the vertical separator at about midpoint of the tank (fig. 5.18). Here, while they are swirled around, two forces work to separate the oil and gas: *gravity* causes the heavier oil to drop to the lower part of the separator, and *the whirling action* causes the heavy oil particles to collect on the walls of the separator. The gas, which still contains some oil particles, rises through the chamber where it is again swirled, and the same forces operate to remove more oil. The gas then rises again and passes through the scrubber dome where the last oil particles are removed. After this final process, the gas is removed through the gas outlet near the top of the separator, and the heavier oil is removed through an outlet at the bottom of the separator.

Horizontal separators

A horizontal separator operates in much the same way as a vertical separator, though, as the name implies, the unit is horizontal instead of upright (fig. 5.19). The same forces of gravity and swirling action are employed, and the oil is removed from the bottom of the unit and the gas from the top.

Horizontal separators may be of either the single-tube or the double-tube design. The double-tube horizontal separator has two horizontal units mounted one above the other and joined by flow channels near the ends of the units. The well fluids enter at one end of the upper unit and are swirled, and the liquids fall through the flow pipe into the liquid reservoir in the lower portion of the bottom unit. The separating process continues in both the upper and lower units, and gas removed from the liquid in the lower unit rises through the flow channel and joins the gas stream leaving the upper separator at the gas outlet. Oil is discharged through a connection at the lower part of the bottom tube.

Separation methods

In order to obtain more complete recovery of liquids, more than one stage of separation is often desirable. When two-stage separation is used, the well fluids pass through either a vertical or horizontal separator for the first stage of separation. The liquid resulting from this stage is then sent into a second separator that operates at a lower pressure, and more gas is removed from the liquid. Any number of separators may be used in stage separation as long as each stage operates at successively lower pressures.

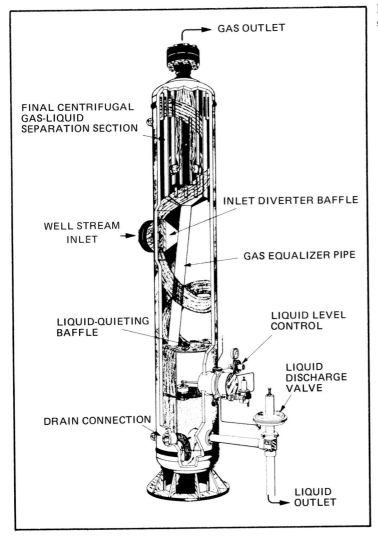

GAS OUTLET

FINAL CENTRIFUGAL
GAS-LIQUID
SEPARATION SECTION

INLET DIVERTER BAFFLE

WELL STREAM
INLET

GAS EQUALIZER PIPE

LIQUID-QUIETING
BAFFLE

LIQUID LEVEL
CONTROL

LIQUID
DISCHARGE
VALVE

DRAIN CONNECTION

LIQUID
OUTLET

Figure 5.18. Conventional vertical separator

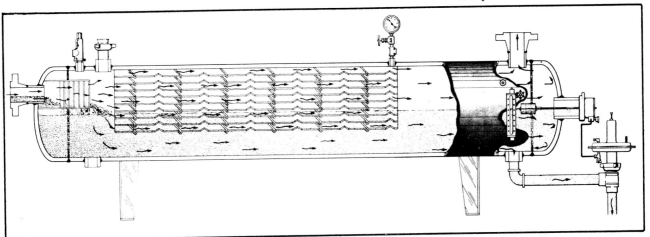

Figure 5.19. Conventional horizontal separator

A low-temperature separation method is used to handle the production from high-pressure gas wells. These wells usually produce a mixture of gas and some light liquids, which must be separated. The removal of water vapor from gas, which is known as dehydration, is important because many pipeline companies will not buy gas containing more than 7 pounds of water per million cubic feet of gas.

The low-temperature separation method uses the cooling effect of expanding high-pressure gas. As the well stream enters the separator at nearly wellhead pressure and moves through a series of coils and an adjustable choke, it expands and cools, allowing the liquids (both condensate and water) to drop to the bottom of the separator. The resulting dry gas is taken out of the separating cycle and moved to the heat exchanger where it is warmed by the well stream; it then moves into the gas gathering system. The condensate goes to a low-pressure vessel, and the wastewater moves into the disposal system.

Treating oil field emulsions

An emulsion is a mixture in which one liquid, termed the dispersed phase, is uniformly distributed (usually as minute globules) in another liquid, called the continuous phase or the dispersion medium. In an oil-water emulsion, the oil is the dispersed phase and the water the dispersion medium. In a water-oil emulsion (fig. 5.20), the reverse is true. The two liquids that form an emulsion, oil and water in this discussion, are <u>immiscible</u> liquids; that is, they are liquids that will not mix together under normal conditions. These two liquids will form an emulsion only if there is sufficient agitation to disperse one liquid as droplets in the other and if there is an

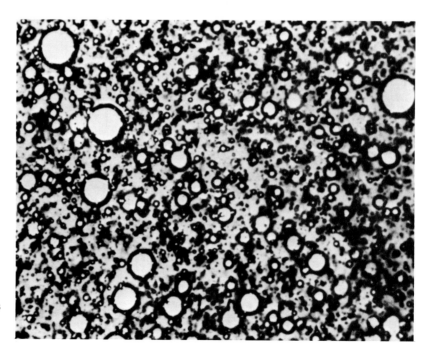

Figure 5.20. Photomicrograph of a water-oil emulsion. The clear circles are water droplets dispersed in oil. Note that the droplets vary in size.

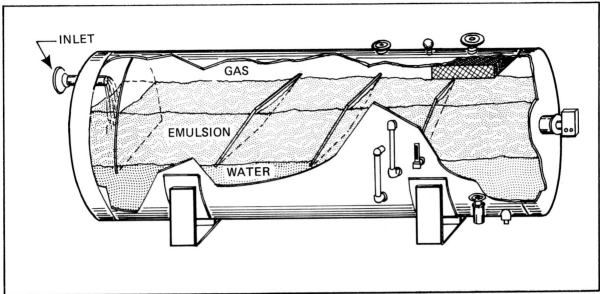

INLET

GAS

EMULSION

WATER

Figure 5.21. Horizontal, three-phase, free-water knockout

emulsifying agent, or emulsifier, present. Emulsifying agents commonly found in petroleum emulsions include asphalt, resinous substances, and oil-soluble organic acids. A stable emulsion is an emulsion that will not break down into its components without some form of treating. Also, an emulsion may be referred to as *tight* (difficult to break) or *loose* (easy to break). Whether an emulsion is tight or loose depends on several factors, including the properties of the oil and water, the percentage of each found in the emulsion, and the type and amount of emulsifier present.

Water must be removed from the oil before the oil can be delivered to the pipeline. Some of the water produced with the oil will not be mixed with it; this is known as *free water*. When given the opportunity, this free water will readily separate from the oil by the force of gravity alone since the water is heavier than the oil. A free-water knockout (sometimes abbreviated as FWKO) is a vertical or horizontal vessel that provides a space for free water to settle out of an emulsion (fig. 5.21). This process occurs before the emulsion is moved through the flow lines to the treating plant.

As mentioned previously, an emulsion must be broken down to separate the oil from water or other contaminants. Treating plants may use a single process or a combination of processes to achieve this goal, depending upon what emulsion is being treated. In a water-in-oil emulsion, there are two forces in direct opposition. One force is the film of emulsifying agent that surrounds the water droplets. This force tends to prevent the droplets from merging together to form larger drops, even when the droplets collide. The other force is the opposite tendency of water droplets to join together to form larger drops. The larger drops yield to the force of gravity and settle out. Therefore, to break down a petroleum emulsion, the properties of the emulsifying agent must be neutralized or destroyed so that the droplets of water may unite. Among the treatment procedures developed to accomplish this are the application of heat, chemicals, and electricity or a combination of these using a heater-treater.

Application of heat

Several theories have been advanced to explain the effect of heat on emulsions. One theory assumes that very small droplets, like those found in emulsions, are in constant motion even when the emulsion itself is at rest. This movement causes both the oil and the water molecules to hit each other. In turn, the water droplets move and strike each other. Heat increases this movement and makes the droplets strike each other with greater force and frequency. When the force of collision is great enough, the surrounding film of the emulsifying agent is ruptured, and the water drops merge together and separate out of the oil. Heat also reduces the viscosity—the resistance to flow—of the oil. This allows the water droplets to collide with even greater force. Again, they coalesce, or merge together, and because these combined droplets are larger and thus heavier, they can settle out of the heated oil more rapidly.

Heat alone does not cause an emulsion to break down, except in rare instances. Usually the application of heat is an auxiliary process to speed up separation. Indeed, if at all possible, heat is eliminated entirely from the treating process. Where it is necessary to use heat, there are many varieties from which to choose. All heaters, however, fall into one of two general categories: direct heaters or indirect heaters.

In a direct heater, the emulsion comes in direct contact with the firebox, or heating element. When operating under proper conditions, direct heaters are the most efficient type of heater. Four basic types of direct heaters are used in the field: tubular heaters; fluid-jacket heaters; internal firebox heaters; and volume, or jug-type, heaters.

An indirect heater consists of three main parts: the body, the firebox, and the flow-tube bundle (fig. 5.22). Heat from the firebox is transferred indirectly through a water bath in the body of the vessel to the emulsion being heated in the flow-tube bundle. An indirect heater is less hazardous to operate than a direct heater because the fire does not touch the flow tubes or come into direct contact with the emulsion. Hot spots, which may crack the tubes, do not form, and the even temperature of the water bath further minimizes salt and scale deposits.

Application of chemicals

Several theories explain the effect that chemicals have on emulsions. One theory suggests that the chemical is used strictly to neutralize

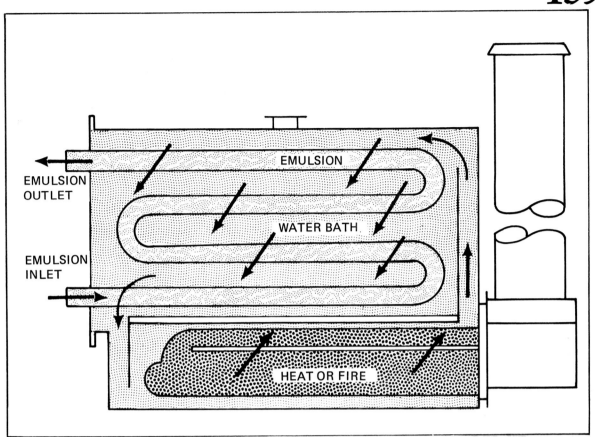

EMULSION OUTLET

EMULSION INLET

EMULSION

WATER BATH

HEAT OR FIRE

Figure 5.22. Indirect heater

the emulsifying agent. Thus, to break a water-in-oil emulsion, another emulsifying agent that would normally produce an oil-in-water emulsion should be added. By attempting to reverse the phases, complete separation is obtained. Another theory suggests that the chemical makes the film of emulsifying agent around the water droplet in a water-in-oil emulsion very rigid (fig. 5.23). Thus, when the enclosed water is expanded by heating, the film is torn, the water droplets can merge, and the emulsion is broken. If no heat is to be applied, the chemical must not only make the film rigid, but also cause it to contract slightly and tear.

The bottle test is used to help determine which chemical can most effectively break the emulsion from a given well, lease, or field (fig. 5.24). Results from a bottle test also indicate the required ratio of treating compound to emulsion—that is, the smallest amount of the proper chemical needed to satisfactorily break the volume of emulsion being produced. Chemicals are applied to the emulsion being treated through a chemical-injection pump. The placement of the chemical pump depends on the particular well and the treating methods being used.

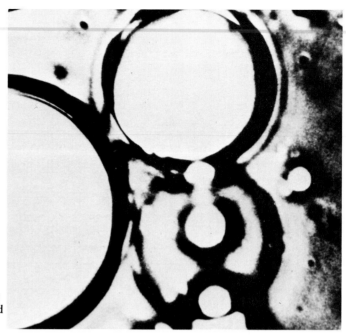

Figure 5.23. This photomicrograph of a water-oil emulsion shows two water droplets touching but unable to merge because of the film around the droplets.

Figure 5.24. Adding chemicals to emulsion samples

Electricity is also used to treat emulsions, usually in conjunction with heat and chemicals. The film the emulsifying agent forms around the water droplets is composed of polar molecules. These are molecules that have both a positive and a negative end, very much like a bar magnet. An electric current disturbs the film of polar molecules around each water droplet by causing the polar molecules to rearrange themselves, thus breaking the tight wall of molecules. The electric field also causes a mutual attraction of emulsion particles, making them rearrange themselves along an electrostatic line of force. The film is no longer stable, and adjacent water droplets coalesce freely until large drops form and settle out by gravity.

Application of electric current

A heater-treater, which is also called a flow treater or an emulsion treater, is a device that combines all the various pieces of equipment used to treat an emulsion in one vessel. Thus, a heater-treater is the vessel in which the effects of chemicals, heat, settling, and often electricity are applied to an emulsion (fig. 5.25). Any or all of the following elements may be included in a heater-treater: oil-gas separator, free-water knockout, heater, water, wash, filter section, stabilizing section, heat exchanger, and electrostatic field. Any one of these functions may be emphasized more than the other, depending on the service for which it is designed. For example, a

Heater-treaters

comb. of all these

Figure 5.25. Vertical heater-treater

heater-treater may have greater free-water capacity and less heating capacity. In addition, each model may be available in a number of sizes so that different volumes of well fluids may be handled (fig. 5.26). Some treaters are designed for use in extremely cold climates; other models are especially designed to treat foaming oil.

Treaters can be operated at atmospheric pressure, but they often operate under low working pressure, and it is often advantageous to use the treater as a low-pressure, second-stage separator as well as a treating unit. Where flow-line pressures are low, it can be used as a primary separator, thus eliminating the need for a regular separator. Flow-line treaters are either vertical or horizontal vessels constructed so that the emulsion, with treating chemical already added, enters the vessel near the top, where the gas is separated from it. Electrostatic treaters are similar to horizontal heater-treaters except that high-voltage, alternating-current, electric grids are added.

Treating natural gas

Field handling of natural gas consists of two basic steps. First, the gas must be separated from free liquids such as crude oil, hydrocarbon condensate, water, and entrained solids. Second, the gas must be processed to remove condensable and recoverable hydrocarbon vapors. In the latter, gas must be treated to remove condensable water vapor, which might cause hydrate formation, and to remove other undesirable components, such as hydrogen sulfide or carbon dioxide.

The well stream—a high-velocity, turbulent, constantly expanding mixture of gases and hydrocarbon liquids, intimately mixed with water vapor, free water, solids, and other contaminants—is passed through a series of separating devices, such as vertical and horizontal separators and heater-treaters, to separate the liquids from the gases. Each of the fluids is treated separately to purify it before it is sold and transported. The primary treatments for natural gas involve the prevention of hydrate formation, dehydration, and the removal of undesirable components.

Prevention of hydrate formation

Most natural gas contains substantial amounts of water vapor. This water vapor must be removed from the gas stream because it will condense into liquid and may cause hydrates to form. A hydrate is a hydrocarbon and water compound that is formed under reduced temperature and pressure in gas gathering, compression, and transmission facilities. Forming as crystals and resembling snow in appearance, hydrates may pack solidly in gas gathering systems, resulting in partially or completely blocked flow lines. Water is always necessary for hydrate formation. Water also almost always accelerates corrosion.

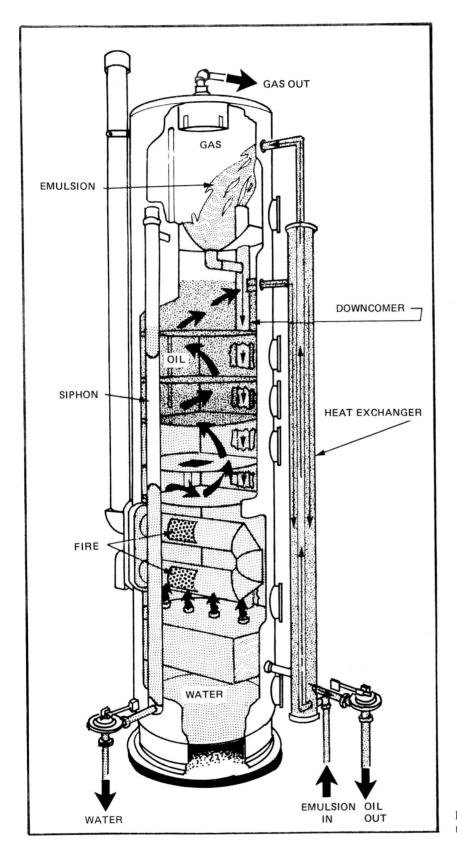

GAS OUT

GAS

EMULSION

DOWNCOMER

OIL

SIPHON

HEAT EXCHANGER

FIRE

WATER

WATER

EMULSION IN

OIL OUT

Figure 5.26. Cutaway view of vertical heater-treater

When gas comes out of the ground, it is at very high pressure, which means that the temperature is also very high. As the gas cools, it can hold less water in the vapor form, and it is when this water vapor condenses into a liquid that hydrate formation becomes a real danger. Hydrate inhibitors are products, such as ammonia, brines, glycol, and methanol, that lower the freezing point of water vapor, thus preventing hydrate formation. In situations in which dehydration is not economical and some measures must be adopted to control hydrate formation, heat is generally applied.

An indirect heater is the most widely used type of heater for natural-gas well streams because it is simple, economical, and a relatively trouble-free piece of equipment. It consists of three basic parts: the heater shell, a removable fire tube and burner assembly, and a removable coil assembly (fig. 5.27). The heater shell is usually

Figure 5.27. Cutaway view of an indirect heater

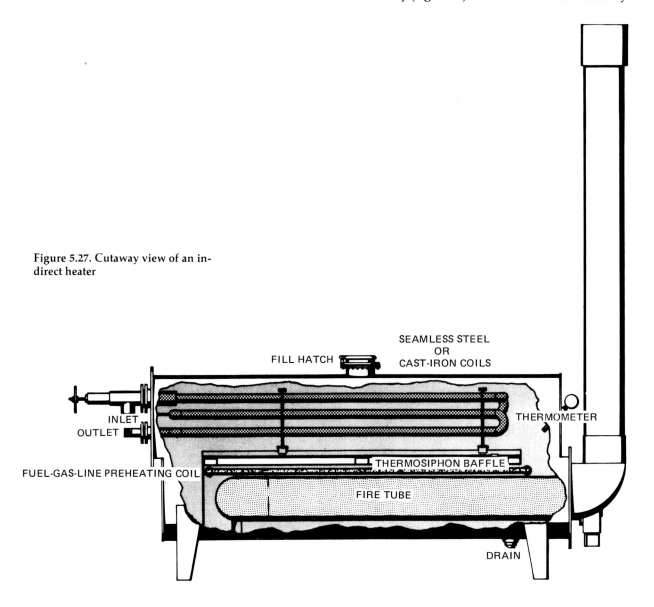

filled with water, which completely covers the fire tube and the coil assembly. The gas moves through the coil assembly, and this assembly is usually designed to withstand shut-in wellhead pressure. The water bath is heated by the fire tube, and the coil assembly is heated by the water.

Dehydration ✗

The term *dehydration* means removal of water. Water vapors, as well as certain other vapors, are removed from gas by either the absorption process or the adsorption process; these two processes result in dehydration. Water vapor may be removed from natural gas by bubbling the gas countercurrently through certain liquids that have a special attraction or affinity for water. When water vapors are removed by this process, the operation is called *absorption.* Some solids also have an affinity for water, and, when gas flows through a bed of such granular solids, the water is retained on the surface of the particles. This process is *adsorption.* The liquid or the solid that has the affinity for water in either process is called a *desiccant.* Removes water

Currently there are two major types of dehydration equipment being used: the liquid-desiccant dehydrator (fig. 5.28) and the

Figure 5.28. Glycol liquid-desiccant dehydrator unit

solid-desiccant dehydrator. Each has its own special advantages and disadvantages, but practically all the gas moved through transmission lines is dehydrated by one or the other of these two methods. Since hydrates do not form in a gas line unless the gas is saturated with so much water vapor that free water forms, dehydration does much to solve the hydrate problem.

Removal of undesirable components

Natural gas well streams often contain hydrogen sulfide and carbon dioxide. These two gases are called acid gases because in the presence of water they form acids or acidic solutions. Unless they are present in very small quantities, they must be removed from a natural gas well stream.

Although there are several processes for removing acid gases from natural gas, the most widely used process in industry is the alkanolamine process. It is a continuous operation liquid process that uses absorption for the acid-gas removal, with subsequent heat addition to strip the acid-gas components from the absorbent solution. The alkanolamine absorbing solution is not selective and absorbs total acid-gas components. Other processes that are used to remove hydrogen sulfide and carbon dioxide are the iron-sponge process, the glycol/amine process, the sulfinol process, and molecular-sieve removal.

THE STORAGE SYSTEM

Oil, water-cut oil, and water produced by the well move from the wellhead or separator through the treating facilities and finally into stock tanks, or a tank battery (fig. 5.29). The number of tanks in a

Figure 5.29. Central treating station with free-water knockout, electro-static treaters, and stock tanks

battery will vary, as will their size, depending on the daily production of the well or wells and the frequency of pipeline runs. The total storage capacity of a tank battery is usually three to seven days' production. Also, since a battery has two or more tanks, one tank can be filling while oil is being run from another.

Before a tank battery is put into operation, each tank is strapped, meaning that the measurements or dimensions of the tank are taken and the amounts of oil that can be contained for each interval of height of the tank are computed. The capacity in barrels according to the height of the liquid in the tank is prepared in table form, and these data make up what is known as the tank table. This table commonly shows the capacity for each ¼ inch from the bottom to the top. The strapping and table preparation is usually done by a third party.

Most tanks are constructed of either bolted or welded steel and are equipped with a bottom drain outlet for draining off basic sediment and water (BS&W). It is sometimes necessary for a workman to enter an empty tank to clean out the collection of paraffin and basic sediment that cannot be removed through the drain outlet.

Oil enters the tank at the top at an inlet opening. The pipeline outlet is usually 1 foot above the bottom of the tank; the space below this outlet provides room for the collection of BS&W. The pipeline outlet valve is closed with a metal seal when the tank is being filled and similarly locked in the open position when the tank is being emptied. This assures both the producer and the pipeline company that only oil in the particular tank will enter the pipeline company's lines.

When measuring or gauging the level of oil in a tank, a steel tape with a plumb bob on the end is lowered into the tank until it just touches the bottom. The highest point at which oil wets the tape shows the level or height of the oil in the tank. By referring to the tank table, the volume of liquid in barrels in the tank is determined. An automatic tank gauge, a newer method of measuring, consists of a steel gauge line contained in a housing; a float on the end of the line rests in the surface of the oil in the tank. The end of the line, which is coiled and counterbalanced outside the tank, runs through a reading box and shows the height of oil in the tank.

MEASURING AND TESTING OIL AND GAS

The volumes of oil, gas, and salt water produced by each lease are usually measured by the lease operator every 24 hours. This operation is important because in many fields the oil or gas is produced in accordance with allowables set by state regulations. These allowables are based on the market demand for the oil or gas and the efficient rate of production for the particular fields. Thus, proper credit must be given to the lease for the oil and gas actually delivered from the lease.

Oil sampling

All oil delivered to pipeline companies is subject to their testing. Therefore, in order to assure that the oil will be accepted, the producer should sample and test the oil in the same manner as prescribed by the pipeline company that purchases the oil. The procedures for taking samples and making water and sediment tests vary from field to field and company to company and must be agreed on by both the buyer and the seller.

Sampling methods

If the oil is in a storage tank, samples can be obtained by the thief sampling or bottle sampling method. In the *thief sampling method*, a thief (a round tube about 15 inches long) is lowered into a tank to the desired level (fig. 5.30). A thief has a spring-operated, sliding valve that can be tripped, thus trapping the sample. The thief is designed so that a sample can be obtained within ½ inch of the bottom of the tank. In the *bottle sampling method*, a 1-quart bottle or beaker is used. It has a stopper with a cord attached to it (fig. 5.31). The sealed bottle is lowered to the desired depth, the stopper is pulled and the bottle is allowed to fill, and then it is pulled up. A small amount of oil is poured off, and the stopper is reinserted.

Figure 5.30. This device called a thief is used to obtain oil samples.

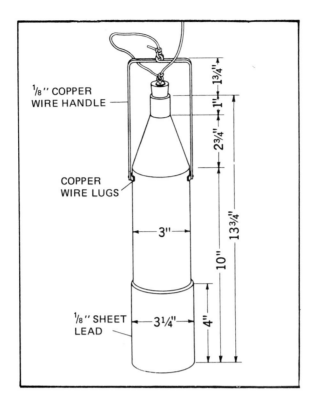

¹⁄₈" COPPER
WIRE HANDLE

COPPER
WIRE LUGS

3"

¹⁄₈" SHEET
LEAD

Figure 5.31. One-quart beaker sampler

Several different types of samples may be taken from a tank of oil, and all parties concerned should agree on which type to take. An *average* sample is one that consists of proportionate parts from all sections of the tank. A *running sample* is one obtained by lowering an unstoppered beaker or bottle from the top of the oil to the level of the bottom of the outlet connection and returning it to the top of the oil at a uniform rate of speed. A *spot sample* is one obtained at some specific location in the tank by means of a thief, bottle, or beaker. There are many other types of tank samples that can be taken, all relating to specific points in the tank.

Types of samples ✗
(3)

daily
monitoring

Gas sampling is always done in the field. The gas-sampling point must be located so that liquids, if condensation does take place, cannot be drawn directly into the sample container. Leaks in any part of the sampling or testing equipment cannot be tolerated, and sampling procedures must assure that containers are purged of all extraneous gases or vapors.

Gas sampling ✗

Crude oil is bought and sold in this country on a volume basis. This volume must be corrected for any BS&W present, and it must also be corrected to the standard base temperature of 60°F. This calls for a series of tests, such as temperature, gravity, and BS&W content. These elements are all measured and gauged in the presence of

Oil measurement and testing

witnesses representing the lease and the pipeline. This information, along with the terms of the lease, producer, and transporter, the number of the tank, the date, and other necessary data are written on the pipeline run ticket, and both representatives sign the ticket.

Temperature measurement

The temperature of oil in lease stock tanks generally is close to that of the air surrounding the tanks unless the oil has just recently been produced and is still carrying an elevated temperature from the subsurface or if the oil has been heated in a treater to separate it from BS&W or salt water. Temperature is usually measured with a special thermometer that is lowered into the oil on a line and then withdrawn to observe the reading.

Gravity and BS&W content measurement

The BS&W content and the API gravity of oil in stock tanks are measured from samples taken from the tanks using a thief or similar method or by drawing oil through sample cocks installed at various levels in the shell of the tank and through which samples can be withdrawn. The requirements for cleanliness of oil vary with individual buyers, but the maximum BS&W content in most states is 1 percent. Most pipelines require that all oil higher than 4 inches below the bottom of the pipeline connection must be acceptable.

The BS&W content of the samples is determined by a centrifuge test, which is also called a shake-out test (fig. 5:32). The glass container in which the test is made is graduated so that the percentages of BS&W can be read directly.

The API gravity of the oil is measured by a hydrometer graduated in °API. If the temperature of the oil is other than 60°F, the gravity reading must be corrected to present the value at 60°F.
because gas expands

Natural gas measuring and testing

Gas testing is an important phase of field handling of natural gas. Although not normally considered as such, it actually is a form of measurement—the determination of the liquid hydrocarbon content of the gas. The results of the field and laboratory tests on the gas may determine how much a seller receives for his gas. Royalty payments may also be directly affected by the results of such tests. Charcoal testing is usually done in the field, while compression testing and fractional analysis are conducted in the laboratory.

Charcoal testing

In a charcoal test, gas is drawn from the stream and passed over activated charcoal. After the adsorption process is complete, the charcoal is taken to a laboratory where the adsorbed liquid is driven off by heat, condensed, and measured. This test is used when other methods of testing either give unsatisfactory results or are too expensive.

Figure 5.32. A high-speed centrifuge is used to determine precise BS&W content.

Compression testing is used extensively on casinghead gas. The sample is compressed in a portable compressor and then cooled in an ice-water bath or in a refrigerated condenser. This is the one form of gas testing that is done completely at the field location, and all equipment used *must* be in top operating condition so that repeatable test data are valid. Compression testing is generally considered to be reliable.

Compression testing ✶

Fractional analysis is used when gas composition must be determined. In this procedure, a sample of the gas stream is obtained in a metal container and shipped to a laboratory where the analysis is performed. The analysis will usually reveal not only the composition in percentage of each hydrocarbon present, but also the gallons per thousand cubic feet by component and the heating value of the gas.

Fractional analysis. ✶

The development of lease automatic custody transfer (LACT) units has changed the processes of measuring, sampling, testing, and transferring oil from a tedious, time-consuming business that

LACT units ✶

required many man-hours and was error-prone into an efficient measuring and recording system that leaves men free to do other operations (fig. 5.33). Despite the complexities of gauging and testing crude oil in the field, automatic equipment can perform the following tasks:

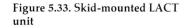
Review

- Measure the volume of the oil and make a record of volume readings.
- Detect the presence of water in the oil stream and indicate the percentage thereof.
- In cases of excessive water, divert the flow into special storage where it will be held for treatment.
- Isolate individual wells on a lease and test them separately from the commingled flow from other wells.
- Determine and record the temperature of the oil.
- Prove the accuracy of flow meters and provide for their calibration when necessary.
- Take samples from the stream in proportion to the rate of flow and hold these for verification by conventional test procedures (fig. 5.34).
- Determine and make a record of the API gravities of the oil produced.
- Switch well production from a full tank to an empty one and turn the oil from the full tank to the pipeline gathering system.
- Shut in the wells and relay an alarm signal to a remote point in case of any malfunction.

Of course, not all LACT installations are as elaborate as the system just described. Operators must design the system that will best meet their individual needs and budgets.

Figure 5.33. Skid-mounted LACT unit

Figure 5.34. A sampler installed on this LACT unit automatically takes samples of the crude oil.

SUMMARY

The steps between the wellhead and pipeline entry involve separation of oil and gas, treating to assist in the separation of oil and BS&W; checking the purity of the oil, gauging the tank and correcting it to 60°F, and checking the API gravity and correcting it to 60°F. These are the steps necessary to enable the crude petroleum to enter into the nation's commerce.

Oil and Gas Pipelines

Pipelines affect the daily lives of millions of people in most parts of the civilized world. Where the greatest concentrations of pipelines are found will also be found the highest standards of living and technological progress. Natural gas and petroleum products are moved through many miles of continuous steel tubes from reservoirs in gulfs, deserts, and distant places.

Offices, factories, and homes are heated and/or air-conditioned with natural gas or the electricity it generates. Food is preserved and prepared with this energy source. Automobile tanks are filled with the grade of gasoline best suited to them. Fuel is brought to electrical power-generating plants and factory complexes. Petrochemical processors make many new and useful products from the feedstocks derived from crude oil and natural gas. The raw materials for these jobs are supplied by pipelines (fig. 6.1).

In almost total silence pipelines move millions of barrels of crude oil, gasoline, and fuel oils, and billions of cubic feet of natural gas in an unbroken stream to consumers (fig. 6.2). These huge carriers operate literally beneath the feet of the public, without disturbing their normal pursuits. Lines are buried and rights-of-way are restored to permit normal use of farms, pastures, and woodlands. A single products line from Texas to New York is capable of transporting gasoline and fuels that would require a railroad train every hour of the day, a tank truck every 12 seconds, or from thirty to forty ocean tankers in continuous service.

Unattended pump stations push crude oil and products through lines designed to transport up to 1,000,000 barrels per day. Natural gas transmission systems move natural gas at equally phenomenal rates. City gates receive gas through stub or lateral lines of transmission systems with a minimum of visual evidence—a few valves, regulators, and a meter house (fig. 6.3).

176

Figure 6.1. Pipelines supply fuel for utility plants such as the one shown here.

Figure 6.2 This compressor plant speeds gas to consumers by pipeline.

Figure 6.3. A scrubber cleans gas at a city gate.

THE DIFFERENCES

The term *pipeline* has many meanings. In a narrow sense, it may mean the pipe and fittings needed to construct facilities for moving commodities in fluid form—gas, liquid, or slurry. In a broader sense, it includes the additional facilities needed to get the job done.

The petroleum industry is largely interested in gas pipelines and oil pipelines. Construction methods are alike, but terminal and intermediate station facilities differ. The gas pipeline has compressors instead of pumps, and control methods for gas differ from those used for oil pipelines. Gas pipelines use pressure control as a basis for operation, whereas liquid pipelines work on the basic principle of controlling rate of flow.

In addition to these mechanical differences, gas and oil pipelines historically have been separate industries, primarily because different regulatory agencies governed their operations. Before the establishment of the U.S. Department of Energy, gas pipelines were regarded as a utility and operated under the regulation of the Federal Power Commission (FPC). Oil pipelines, on the other hand, were classified as common carriers and operated under Interstate Commerce Commission (ICC) regulations. At present, transportation in both industries is under the control of the U.S. Department of Transportation, and acquisition and sale in both industries are controlled by the Federal Energy Regulatory Commission (FERC), a branch of the U.S. Department of Energy.

CRUDE-OIL AND PRODUCTS PIPELINES

✻ Beginnings

With the discovery of oil in Titusville, Pennsylvania, in 1859 came the birth not only of the oil industry in America, but of the related industries that sprang up to process and transport the crude and refined products to other parts of the country (fig. 6.4). Demand for the oil was pressing, and many competed for the job of hauling the oil wherever it was needed. The first solution was proposed by the teamsters, who set up a massive system of boats, barges, and horse-drawn carts and transported the oil to refineries in what turned out to be a rather expensive and sometimes dangerous fashion. The railroads promptly joined in the competition, and within a few years the rail network provided crude oil to outlets in Cleveland and New York, but the problem of how to get the oil to the railroad and shipping stations remained. The teamsters were willing to haul the crude in heavy barrels of about 360 pounds each, and as

Figure 6.4. Petroleum products were transported with horse-drawn carts and Model T trucks before products pipelines became widespread.
(Courtesy of Humanities Research Center, The University of Texas at Austin)

many as 2,000 teams a day lumbered into Titusville through the mud in order to do so. But slippery roads and high prices were an incentive to come up with yet another system: pipelines.

The railroad companies were the first to construct and buy pipelines of their own or to form exclusive arrangements with pipeline transportation companies. In an effort to maintain monopolistic control over the oil transportation business, the railroads attempted to prevent any other pipeline companies from crossing their rail lines (fig. 6.5). But public sentiment was against monopolies, and the Pennsylvania and Ohio legislatures passed laws in 1872 that granted common-carrier pipelines the privilege of eminent domain in obtaining their rights-of-way. These acts were the prelude to the development of oil trunkline systems, because main trunk pipelines could connect the field directly to the refineries and provide more economical transportation.

Until 1900, crude-oil production was centered in Pennsylvania, West Virginia, Ohio, and other eastern states, and refineries were also centered around the eastern population centers. But between

Crude-oil pipelines ☆

Figure 6.5. Denied the right to cross a railroad, a pipeline company used tank wagons to move crude oil across the tracks until the courts ruled in its favor against the railroad.

1901 and 1905, oil was discovered in Texas, Kansas, Oklahoma, Louisiana, and California, and the eastern refineries were forced to seek additional crude supplies from the western centers of production. By 1914 the mid-continent oil fields supplied over 60 percent of the crude oil to the eastern refineries, and by 1940 they were supplying over 85 percent. A network of crude-oil trunk pipelines was built to connect the source of supply with the refining centers, but a large part of transporting was done by ship as well. The combined system of shipping and pipelines worked quite well until World War II, when enemy submarines sank many of the oil tankers destined for wartime industries on the East Coast. So, the federal government joined forces with the petroleum industry and constructed the first large-diameter crude-oil pipeline called the Big Inch, and the refined products line, called the Little Big Inch. The Big Inch was 24 inches in diameter, while the Little Big Inch had a 20-inch diameter.

Products pipelines

The first batching (shipping one petroleum product after another through the same pipeline) of refined products was performed in 1901 in Pennsylvania, but construction of products pipelines did not begin in earnest until 1930, when the growth of large population centers in the Midwest had created new marketing areas for refined products. Because of the Depression, the established oil marketers were battling more fiercely than ever for a share of the market. Competition demanded that the least expensive method of transportation be employed from the refinery to the market. Pipelines designed to transport many grades of refined products were the answer. As a result, 3,000 miles of products pipelines were placed in operation during 1930–31. In certain instances, older crude lines were cleaned and the direction of flow reversed to move products from the East Coast to the Midwest.

Postwar developments

Construction and production in oil pipelines increased tremendously during World War II and afterwards. From prewar deliveries of less than 50,000 barrels, daily pipeline shipments eastward soared to a maximum of 754,000 barrels, with the companies east of the Rockies increasing their total daily movements about 60 percent between 1941 and 1945. Companies discovered that large-diameter trunklines proved to have operating flexibility previously considered available only in smaller lines and that the larger lines reduced transportation costs per barrel considerably. Pipelines devoted to the transportation of liquids increased from 124,000 miles in 1948 to more than 222,000 miles in 1976 (fig. 6.6). Since 1976, actual mileage has declined but quantities shipped have steadily risen due to larger-diameter lines and the *looping of long lines,* that is, laying additional lines alongside existing pipelines.

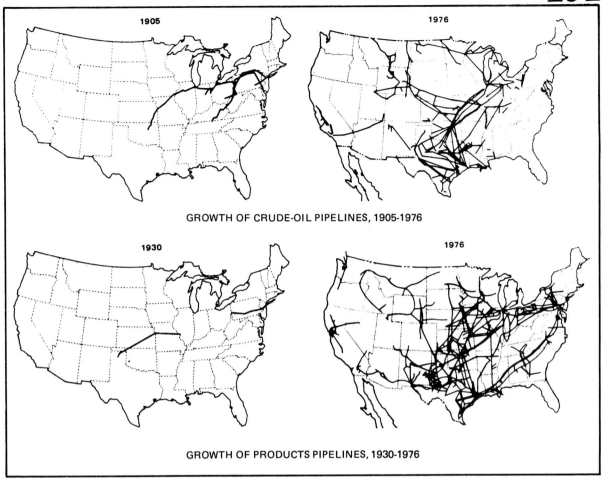

1905 1976

GROWTH OF CRUDE-OIL PIPELINES, 1905-1976

1930 1976

GROWTH OF PRODUCTS PIPELINES, 1930-1976

Figure 6.6. Pipeline capacities in the United States have increased tremendously, with the largest growth taking place during and after World War II.

State and federal regulations

In an industry where crude oil and refined products are shipped regularly, accurate recording of shipments sent and received can mean the difference between profit and loss and even between legal and illegal operation. Some states, like Texas, require the pipeline companies to keep track of individual and connected shippers to see that each company is complying with the established monthly proration schedules. Monthly forms are filed with the state to indicate the quantity of oil taken from each lease. The federal government also imposes stringent controls on various aspects of the pipeline industry through the Department of Transportation (DOT), the Department of Energy (DOE), and the Occupational Safety and Health Administration (OSHA).

182

Figure 6.7. Shot from an elevation of 27,000 feet, this southwestern oil and gas field is a maze of wells (light spots) and flow lines (white lines).

Field gathering systems

An oil field may have several hundred wells, with flow lines that carry crude oil from the wells to the lease tanks (fig. 6.7). Various tanks and treating vessels are often a part of the field gathering system, but lines can take crude oil away without having tanks or other ground equipment except for printing meters to register the number of barrels taken.

After the oil is gathered from the field and has been treated, measured, and tested, it is ready for the pipeline—a major network of small and large arteries installed by the pipeline company to give oil producers an outlet to market.

To move the oil into and through the pipeline, pressure is required. This pressure is supplied by pumps in a pumping station. Functionally, pump stations are either gathering stations or trunkline stations or a combination of both. A gathering station is located in or near an oil field and receives oil through a pipeline gathering system from the producers' tanks. From the gathering station, oil is relayed to a trunkline station, which is located on the main pipeline, or trunkline. Of much greater capacity, the trunkline station relays the oil to refineries or shipping terminals. Since the pressure gradually drops as the oil is moved through the line, booster pump stations are spaced along the trunkline as needed. Along the line, tank farms serve as receiving and holding stations. Oil coming in and leaving tank farms and pumping stations is regulated by manifolds.

Pumping station operation

Numerous reciprocating pumps are still used at gathering stations, where often the crude gathered is entering a stream and needs the strong drive provided by reciprocating pumps. The gathering station may include one or more pumps and may move from a hundred to several thousand barrels of oil daily, coming in from various producers' tanks and gathering station tanks. Pumping units usually consist of electric-drive reciprocating or centrifugal pumps. Internal-combustion engines have been almost totally displaced by electric motors as prime movers (fig. 6.8).

Gathering stations

Figure 6.8. Pumps and prime movers at a gathering station

The method of operating a gathering station depends on its size and function. At tanks where custody transfer occurs, the pumps are activated by a gauger, who measures the volume and draws samples for analysis before pumping begins. On leases where LACT units are installed, pumps are started automatically or by remote control (fig. 6.9). After the oil is received at the gathering station, it is pumped either to another gathering station closer to the trunkline or directly to a trunkline station.

Trunkline stations

Trunkline stations are located on the main petroleum-carrying arteries. A trunkline station might be set up to pump crude oil to refineries or refined products to marketing terminals. A trunkline station might also serve as a gathering station if near the oil source, but most relay pumped oil.

Pumps most commonly used in trunkline stations today are typically high-speed centrifugal units having a direct connection to electric motors. Internal-combustion engines and gas turbines have lost favor due to increases in both fuel and maintenance costs. In a large station, the pumps are placed in series so that each pump handles the total flow, imparting its share of pressure to the oil.

Along the trunkline are booster stations, positioned in balance hydraulically. This means that each booster station has the same work load to perform because the pipeline's profile and its hydraulic head (pressure required to overcome the inertia, gravity, and friction of the liquid on the inside surface of the pipe) have been considered in choosing the sites of the booster stations.

Station tank farms

Tank farms are to pipelines what railway yards are to railroads. They are places where oil in transit may be temporarily sidetracked for sorting, measuring, rerouting, or simply holding during repairs on a line or station. Tank farms may also be receiving stations where oil comes in from the producing fields or from other carriers to be injected into the pipeline transportation system (fig. 6.10). Trunklines bring crude oil belonging to many different shippers to the tank farm. By segregating shipments in the tanks, the pipeline company can make deliveries to various owners at refineries or terminals.

Pump station manifold

Tank farm pipelines converge at a station manifold (fig. 6.11). The manifold permits the switching of the oil stream to the proper destination. It can be very complex as in a main station or simple as in a booster station. A manifold might connect a mainline, a field gathering line, several tanks, and one or more pumps.

This network of lines and valves, operated by the tank farm and station personnel, can (1) pump oil through the trunkline with tanks inactive, (2) receive production from the field into any tank, (3) receive from a trunkline into any tank, (4) transfer from one tank to another, (5) pump from any tank into the trunkline, (6) isolate all

Figure 6.9. A control room for a modern pipeline system

Figure 6.10. Tank farm and pump station at a pipeline junction. Tank farm pipelines converge at the station manifold. Note the position of the floating roofs on the tanks.

Figure 6.11. A manifold at a pump station and tank farm

pumps and tanks while the trunkline station upstream pumps through, or (7) inject oil from any tank into oil being pumped through the trunkline.

Control of oil movements

Pipeline shipping of crude oil is based on large shipments, high throughput, and efficient operation to reduce costs to a minimum for the benefit of the shippers. Hence, a single shipment, or batch, must consist of a minimum volume of several thousand barrels. Any single pipeline may handle several grades of oil for each of several shippers. The shipment is scheduled by the pipeline scheduler to leave a stated point of origin on a stated date and to be delivered to a destination point on a set date. The shipper must have tank space to receive the grade of oil at the destination.

A typical shipment might be accumulated over a period of several days. Each day a part of the shipment is delivered from the leases to pipeline company tanks to be held until the required volume is ready for delivery to the trunkline. The pipeline takes custody at the lease where the oil is produced. It is held for the account of the shipper who either produced it or bought it. Suppose transit time is ten days and ten different shippers regularly use a pipeline. At any given time each of these shippers might have several shipments in the line, and the pipeline company might have in the line and in its tanks more than a million barrels of oil, all of which belongs to the shippers. As oil is pumped in at the upstream end, an equal volume is pumped out at the downstream end. Each shipper, therefore, is continually receiving deliveries and putting more oil in the line. Thus, the shipper always has a balance of oil in the system. While his oil is in transit, a shipper may trade it to another shipper for oil that was shipped earlier. Then the pipeline changes the route and delivers it to the new owner at a different destination. This buying, selling, trading, and rerouting of shipments is a fact of life in pipeline operation.

Just as a railway freight shipment may travel on more than one railroad in transit, so a shipment of crude oil may travel on more than one pipeline system between origin and destination of the shipment. Requests for shipping space in one section of a line may be greater than those in other sections of the same line due to transfers to another pipeline system at some point miles downstream of the originating station. The second line must be prepared to receive the diverted shipment, and the originating line must pump from tankage at the diversion point while the diverted shipment is being withdrawn from the line. Otherwise, oil movements on the downstream sections of the originating line would come to a standstill.

Scheduling

To handle all the operations involved in pipelining, a coordinator or scheduler works with the shippers to set up a mutually agreed upon schedule. After the total business has been received and the barrel-per-day line rates have been established, required pumping units are selected to move the material to its destination.

On lines with many pump stations and pumping units, computer programs determine the stations to be operated and the exact pumping unit combinations to be used to obtain the desired flow rate at minimum power cost. The movement of crude oil is scheduled according to the projected dates of both accumulation from producing areas and connecting carrier sources. Though tanks are common items at points of origin and at terminals, modern pipeline systems are designed with a minimum of operating tankage. This limited availability of tank storage is a major problem in pipeline scheduling. The sequencing of batches of oil to arrive at final destination or intermediate delivery points for barge or tanker loading requires considerable skill on the part of the scheduler. Computers are used on the modern pipeline to develop schedules, project the schedules to completion, print out the pertinent information of delivery times and dates, and to inject and switch instructions needed to implement the schedules (fig. 6.12).

Figure 6.12. An operator uses a computer console to control the movement of the oil through the pipeline. Tri-color video displays enable him to view any aspect of the modern products pipeline pumping station. Panels in the background contain a typical format of station piping, valves, gravity recorders, tank level indicator, run ticket printers, and other functions.

After the schedule has been determined, a pipeline dispatcher, sometimes called a line operator or oil movement controller, communicates with other points on the pipeline system. Using a computer console, he controls the pumping stations hundreds of miles away and monitors pressures of lines, rates of flow into and out of the pipeline system, and gravities of the various crude-oil streams.

In executing the schedule, the dispatcher operates motor valves, starts and stops pumps, and performs other operations in the system through computer-assisted remote control. As the dispatcher executes the schedules, records are made to show how, when, and what quantity and quality were delivered. The dispatcher is also responsible for the security of the lines.

Dispatching

Along with the scheduler who devises the plan and the dispatcher who executes it, an oil measurements group has the job of preserving the quality and quantity of material tendered to the pipeline by the shipper. This group checks methods used by field personnel to measure the quantity of oil by meters and tank gauges. Testing procedures and sampling devices are constantly monitored.

Testing

The run ticket is the basic accounting document in the buying and selling of millions of barrels of crude oil each day. Every time custody of oil changes hands, a run ticket is made and signed by the receiver and the deliveryman. This ticket serves as a record and a receipt for all oil handled by the pipelines. It describes the oil in terms of grade, gravity, BS&W content, and the number of barrels as determined by tank gauges or by meters. In pipeline operations, control is essential to insure the proper handling of oil movements. Records are maintained and used many months after the oil has been delivered to its destination.

Accounting

Figure 6.13. The Chinese were the first to pipe natural gas, using bamboo pipes. This fairly recent photo shows crude gas piping in use in Tseliutsing, Szechwan Province. *(Courtesy of American Gas Association)*

Figure 6.14. This early pipeline is constructed of wooden staves and hoops. *(Courtesy of American Petroleum Institute)*

NATURAL GAS PIPELINES

Although people knew about the uses of natural gas 3,000 years ago when the Chinese piped natural gas through hollow bamboo poles (fig. 6.13), widespread use of natural gas did not develop until it became easily available at competitive prices.

Historical background

Aaron Hart, a gunsmith, was the first American to discover a natural-gas well in 1821. He had drilled only 17 feet when a hissing sound indicated that he had not struck water but something unexpected—gas; thus, the first natural-gas well was drilled on the American continent. Hart promptly experimented with the gas to see what could be done with it and, before long, had strung together a few hollowed logs as a crude pipeline (fig. 6.14). With this primitive system, he managed to light some buildings nearby, and this was the beginning of the natural gas industry.

From then on, the problem that took longest to solve was finding a practical means of transmitting gas from the fields where it was produced to the cities and factories where it could be used. By the beginning of the twentieth century, natural gas was available as a fuel for homes and industries (fig. 6.15), but costs were high because the

Figure 6.15. Gaslights were a nineteenth-century luxury. Note the gas table lamp. *(Courtesy of American Petroleum Institute)*

delivery system was still inefficient. As a result, other fuels including manufactured or synthetic gas were used in place of natural gas.

Synthetic gas had an important effect on the eventual development of the natural gas industry because it was so much cleaner and easier to use than some of the other fuels in common use at the time. Synthetic gas was produced in Europe and America by heating coal, coke, and other solid fuels and then passing steam over them. But, because of the high price, manufactured gas was not widely used in the United States until the 1920s.

The earliest pipelines

Constructing the first natural gas pipelines was backbreaking work, especially as heavy machinery had not yet replaced horses and mules (fig. 6.16). For the first two decades of the twentieth century, the digging was done by hand with picks and shovels, aided by dynamite in the toughest places. Even where the soil was soft, the pipeliners had to contend with the physical difficulties of constructing lines through some of the most remote and dangerous countryside—areas plagued with rattlesnakes and raging sandstorms.

Figure 6.16. True horsepower was used in early-day construction of pipelines and compressor stations. *(Courtesy of El Paso Natural Gas Company)*

The first large-scale natural gas transmission lines came about as a direct result of World War II. After the war ended, private industry bought the crude-oil and products pipelines, the Big Inch and the Little Big Inch, and converted them to natural-gas transmission lines, thereby solving the problem of supplying the gas to the markets at rates competitive with other fuels.

Since 1950, the natural gas industry has grown tremendously as technological advances cut the cost of installing pipe. From 1950 to 1975, the number of total miles of gas pipeline has tripled, and currently more than a quarter-million miles of gas pipelines are in use across the United States (fig. 6.17). Of these, about 190,000 miles are transmission trunklines, with the remaining mileage consisting largely of field gathering lines. Table 6.1 shows the location of these pipelines and the distribution of gas customers by state. More than 1,000 compressor stations are associated with the trunklines, using over 12 million horsepower to drive the compressors. In addition to the trunkline stations, another 1,000 compressor stations for field gathering and other uses require 2.5 million horsepower from prime movers in the form of electric motors, turbines, and internal-combustion engines.

Modernization of transmission systems

The system of equipment used for collecting, conditioning, and transmitting gas to its primary destination depends on the individual situation, but necessary to any gas gathering system is equipment for (1) conditioning the gas so it will flow safely and steadily and (2) controlling, measuring, and recording its flow through the pipeline.

Gas gathering systems

Conditioning equipment such as separators, heaters, dehydrators, and compressors are located at the wellhead where the gas first reaches the surface or at other locations in the field. Each piece of equipment has its particular function related to the safe and steady flow of gas from the wellhead to the pipeline and finally to its destination often thousands of miles away.

Separators isolate components flowing in the line. Heaters prevent hydrate formation by raising the temperature of the gas to a safe level until it reaches the next stage of conditioning, and dehydrators remove water vapor from the gas.

Large compressors are used to compress the gas up to or in excess of a hundred times the normal atmospheric pressure. Usually large reciprocating compressors driven by gas engines are used, but centrifugal units driven by gas turbines or electric motors are also used. Large compressor stations along the pipeline often use natural gas from the pipeline for fuel. To do this, the high pressure of the gas is lowered to a usable pressure by the use of regulators.

Conditioning equipment

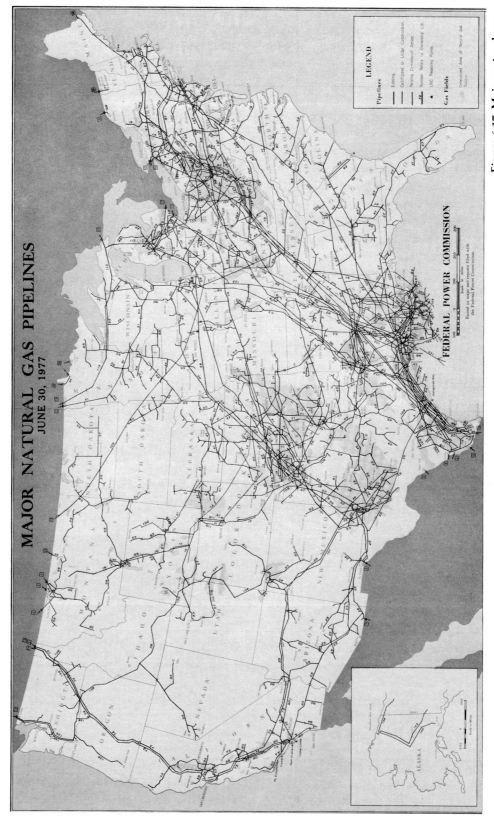

Figure 6.17. Major natural gas pipelines in the United States in 1977

Table 6.1
Transmission Pipelines and Natural Gas
Customers by State

State	Transmission Pipelines (miles)	Gas Customers (thousands)
Alabama	5,301	644.4
Alaska	115	30.4
Arizona	5,041	561.0
California	7,813	6,632.2
Colorado	6,219	726.6
Connecticut	538	390.2
Delaware	227	82.4
District of Columbia	23	153.2
Florida	3,101	409.9
Georgia	4,982	927.3
Hawaii	0	34.5
Idaho	1,312	109.0
Illinois	9,955	3,158.3
Indiana	5,655	1,196.3
Iowa	6,142	702.6
Kansas	15,547	679.0
Kentucky	6,950	627.4
Louisiana	21,697	943.3
Maine	538	17.6
Maryland	730	773.8
Massachusetts	789	1,052.4
Michigan	6,891	2,244.4
Minnesota	3,983	727.3
Mississippi	9,355	383.3
Missouri	4,153	1,177.5
Montana	3,041	176.1
Nebraska	7,448	411.2
Nevada	1,236	118.7
New Hampshire	129	46.2
New Jersey	1,310	1,823.9
New Mexico	6,023	288.7
New York	4,232	3,996.3
North Carolina	2,291	342.2
North Dakota	1,111	74.9
Ohio	10,218	2,756.3
Oklahoma	11,136	753.9
Oregon	1,167	250.8
Pennsylvania	11,983	2,327.1
Rhode Island	53	160.8
South Carolina	2,315	285.9
South Dakota	942	94.7
Tennessee	5,116	494.0
Texas	38,295	3,029.1
Utah	909	310.0
Vermont	60	16.6
Virginia	2,352	526.1
Washington	1,707	348.8
West Virginia	5,830	396.1
Wisconsin	3,166	959.0
Wyoming	2,885	103.5
Total U. S.	252,012	44,941.5

Source: Interstate Natural Gas Association of America, Washington, D. C.

Controlling and measuring flow

Compressed gas exhibits a complex behavior pattern, and, in order to operate a gas pipeline properly, most of the variables of the gas must be measured and controlled. Commonly used to measure the volume of natural gas is the orifice meter, although the turbine meter is replacing it. Turbine meters are ideally suited to easy transmission of measurements via electronic means and are more accurate than orifice meters over a wider range of flow rates.

Modern gas pipelines are also equipped with devices and instruments that measure and record density, dew point, temperature, and pressure. Recording gravitometers are used to measure and record the specific gravity of natural gas, which is needed to calculate gas flow. Pertinent information is gathered by electronic data recorders and processors and is sent to an office for analysis.

Automation

Modern gas pipelines have become so automated that, in most cases, they are capable of operating under command of a *computer system* that coordinates the operation of all valves, prime movers, and conditioning equipment. The computer receives input from each part of the system, including all of the conditioning and measuring equipment. In case of malfunction at any point in the process, the computer searches its program for possible corrective actions and simultaneously sounds alarms at the appropriate control points (fig. 6.18).

Figure 6.18. A computerized gas control center keeps tab on deliveries throughout the pipeline system. *(Courtesy of El Paso Natural Gas Company)*

An interesting aspect of natural-gas pipelines is the introduction of odorants into the gas system. Natural gas is apt to be almost odorless as it comes from the well or processing facilities. If the gas is destined for use as a fuel in homes or industry, a compound called _mercaptan_ is used to odorize the gas so that it can be easily detected when its presence in the atmosphere reaches a concentration of 1 percent. Gas and air mixed in this concentration are not hazardous, while a mixture containing 5 percent gas would be explosive. The odorant makes leaks or other unburned discharges of the gas quite evident long before a real hazard exists. Odorants injected into the gas burned in homes or industry do not create odors while burning or leave troublesome residue.

Odorants are not introduced into gas sent to petrochemical plants where it is used as a feedstock for producing other commodities such as plastics. Such use might cause product contamination and would certainly waste mercaptan.

Odorants

PIPELINE CONSTRUCTION

Before construction begins on a modern pipeline, months and sometimes years of engineering studies and surveys of potential reservoirs and markets precede the final decision to build the line. Routes are surveyed by aerial photography and surface mapping; occasionally helicopters are used for reconnaissance and rapid transportation in difficult terrain. Before the pipeline superintendent goes out to begin construction, he has in his possession several guidelines by which he determines all operations: maps, a line list, and contract specifications. His maps show in accurate detail all surface features affecting construction. The line list sets out in sequence the names of all landowners, the number of linear rods of line to be built on each piece of property, and any written limitations or restrictions. Included are copies of permits for crossing roads, rivers, and other public property. Specifications in the contract cover every planned operation and as many eventualities as possible.

Laying pipe on land

The spread—that is, the necessary equipment and crew involved in building a pipeline—must be assembled by the pipeline builder. A spread can be composed of as many as 250 to 300 men in a normal operation and up to 500 in a very large operation. The amount of construction equipment depends on the variety and difficulty of terrain; stream crossings, marshes, bogs, heavily timbered forests, steep slopes, or rocky ground can require different pieces of machinery. The pipeline contractor might rent rather than buy the necessary machines since outfitting a big-inch (large-diameter) pipeline spread can be a multimillion-dollar operation. A spread of

Assembling the spread

250 to 300 men can move at a rate of 3 miles a day with a distance of sometimes 10 or 15 miles separating the beginning of the work crew from the end.

Clearing right-of-way

immonent domain — w/o regard to ownership
"reasonable market value"

Right-of-way is the legal right of passage over another person's land; in practice it is usually a cleared strip of land from 50 to 75 feet wide, depending on the size of the pipe and the type of terrain. The clearing crews open fences and build gates, cattle guards, and bridges as the first segment of the spread moves up on the job. Salable timber cut by clearing crews is stacked; the rest is cut and burned. Grading and completion of a roadway capable of supporting all vehicles follow. The road must be large enough for the largest side-boom tractor and other necessary equipment. In rocky terrain, a machine equipped with a ripper that extends several feet into the ground is often used to loosen rocks for removal before the ditching operation begins (fig. 6.19).

Ditching

A ditch is made by loose-dirt ditching machines (fig. 6.20). or by wagon drills suspended from side-boom tractors, and dynamite blasting for very hard rock surfaces is the next step in preparing to lay pipe. The ditch must be at least 12 inches wider than the pipe diameter, and it must be able to contain the pipe and permit its being lowered in and backfilled without damaging the pipe. Ditches must be deep enough to ensure that they will not interfere with plowing and other normal land use. The Department of Transportation requires a minimum of 36 inches of cover.

Figure 6.19. Right-of-way is cleared, and often a machine such as the one shown here loosens large rocks for removal before ditching operation begins.

Pipe is purchased and transported to the ditching sites by the pipeline contractor or its subcontractor; then the jobs of yard coating and double jointing begin. Yard coating includes cleaning, priming, coating, and wrapping the pipe, leaving only enough of the pipe ends exposed to permit welding. Double jointing is the welding of two sections of pipe to form one piece up to 80 feet in length. Often as many as seven out of every ten pieces of pipe must be bent to fit the ditch before it is welded together (fig. 6.21). Special equipment allows the pipe to be bent on location (fig. 6.22). A bending shoe—an attachment that works off the side-boom tractor and winch—can be used for small-diameter pipe. A bending mandrel, which keeps large-diameter pipe from buckling and wrinkling when bent, permits approximately twice as much bend in the new high-test, thin-wall pipes as the old methods allowed.

Before the pipe is welded in place, the ends must be absolutely clean of all dirt, scale, and coating. Sometimes the beveled edges of the joint must be recut before the two pipe ends are aligned. To accomplish alignment, clamps are used outside on small-diameter pipe and inside on larger-diameter pipe; the side-boom tractor and winches lower the pipe into place and hold it while skids are put under it and the initial welds are made. The welds are then inspected visually and by X rays before the pipe is coated and wrapped. A machine cleans the pipeline with rotating brushes, and a layer of fast-drying enamel is applied to aid in binding the wrapping at the joints. Then a protective coating of coal tar or asphalt is applied; a layer of glass fiber follows, coated at temperatures of 475 to 525 degrees Fahrenheit, and a final coating of asbestos felt or tar paper is wrapped around the whole thing to protect the coating from damage by skids, slings, or rocks during lowering of the line and backfilling operations.

In some conditions pipe is lowered into the ditch in conjunction with the coating and wrapping operation. This method eliminates the two steps of lowering the pipe to skids and picking it up later for final placement.

Crossing preexisting pipelines requires going under the line already in place. In some situations six or more side-boom tractors must be used in the operation. Creek crossings and steep terrain also require the skillful maneuvering of side-boom operators as they move long sections of pipe into position.

Highway, railroad, and river crossings leave openings in the line that are closed by the tie-in crew, a miniature spread that joins the segments into one continuous line. At tie-ins, extra pipe is cut off and bevels made, welds are made, and protective coatings are put on, until the entire line is complete.

Figure 6.20. A ditching machine is used where soil permits to rapidly dig a slant-sided ditch for the pipe.

Figure 6.21. Pipe must be bent to match the profile of the terrain.
(Courtesy of El Paso Natural Gas Company)

Figure 6.22. Pipe is bent by placing individual lengths of it in a bending machine before it is welded to the line. *(Courtesy of El Paso Natural Gas Company)*

Figure 6.23. A joint of pipe has just been placed over an internal line-up clamp. The man at left controls the operation of the expanding blocks that grip the internal surface of the pipe. *(Courtesy of El Paso Natural Gas Company)*

Figure 6.24. This cleaning and priming machine carries a supply of priming liquid in the sled at right. The tractor supports the pipe ahead of the machine and tows the sled.

Figure 6.25. While the coating and wrapping machine is being used, the tractor uses its side boom to support the pipe ahead of the machine and tows a kettle containing the coating material.

Figure 6.26. This wrapping machine applies overlapping layers of fiber-glass material and craft paper. The man at lower right is checking quality of the job with an electrical holiday detector—a device that locates weak spots (holidays) in pipeline coatings.

Figure 6.27. The side boom lowers the pipe into the ditch carefully to avoid damaging the coating and wrapping.

Figure 6.28. Some tie-in welds are made in the ditch. Usually these pipe ends are allowed to overlap and are carefully measured and cut so ends can be aligned with minimum manipulation.

Figure 6.29. The versatile bulldozer is the most popular means of backfilling, although tractors with an extended side boom and a heavy dragline device are often used on farmland. *(Courtesy of El Paso Natural Gas Company)*

Figure 6.30. After construction is completed, a neatly restored right-of-way allows this land to once again produce crops.

Laying pipe offshore

Drilling and pipelining offshore in shallower depths has been well established for quite some time. The necessary technology has been developed, and various methods of laying pipe and drilling for oil offshore are available to the industry. More modern approaches to constructing pipelines offshore include the use of various types of barges.

Conventional lay barge

Offshore lines are laid by pipe-laying barges, or simply *lay barges.* A lay barge is a complete seagoing plant that allows the pipeline to be continuously assembled and laid along the selected right-of-way on the ocean floor, or, in shallower waters, in dredged trenches on the ocean floor. When used in conjunction with supporting tugs and an anchoring system, the lay barge can be self-sufficient for months at a time.

An eight-point mooring system of wire rope and anchors holds the lay barge in a precise heading to prevent buckling of the pipe as it is laid. The system also propels the barge as anchor lines are reeled in and out. As the barge progresses to the end of the lines, the mooring system is moved ahead by anchor-handling tugs.

The line pipe is brought by pipe barge from yards on shore and stored aboard the lay barge for addition to the lengthening pipeline. A line-up device aligns the joints of pipe as they are joined to the pipeline. Welding, coating, and inspection (X raying) are handled at stations, or work areas, along the length of the lay barge deck (fig. 6.31). The completed pipeline is lowered into the water by way of an inclined ramp on the barge and a *stinger.* The stinger attaches to the ramp and guides the pipeline to the seafloor at the proper angle (fig. 6.32). The pipeline is coated with a high-density cement to overcome buoyancy so it can be sunk into place. To prevent cracking of this concrete coating or buckling of the pipeline, a catenary, or slight

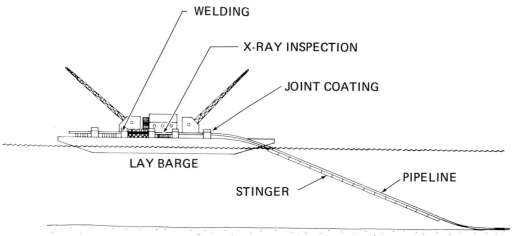

Figure 6.31. A lay barge is a complete seagoing pipe-laying plant.

Figure 6.32. The completed pipeline is lowered into the water by way of an inclined ramp on the lay barge and a stinger attached to the ramp. *(Courtesy of American Petroleum Institute)*

Figure 6.33. A pontoon hitched to the end of the pipe ramp will allow the safe descent of the pipe to the seafloor.

vertical curve in the line, is necessary. An attachment called a *pontoon* is sometimes added to the stinger for deepwater operations (fig. 6.33). The pontoon is control flooded to lower the line toward the seafloor at a proper catenary angle to prevent overstressing of the pipeline.

The method used to keep the pipeline on the bottom and out of danger varies with the topography of the seafloor. On rocky bottoms, the line is fastened to the seafloor with pipeline anchors.

Bury barge

On softer bottoms, a bury barge, or pipe-trenching barge, with a sled is used to bury the pipeline (fig. 6.34). The sled, which is attached to the submerged line, moves along the line on the seafloor and uses a high-pressure jetting action to form a trench in which the pipeline will rest. Eventually, the pipeline is covered by migrating fill material. Burying the pipe minimizes the danger of its being snagged by a dragging anchor or trawl net.

Figure 6.34. With a dredging sled mounted on its stern, a bury barge forms a trench on the ocean floor for the pipe and then covers it with fill material. On the trenching barge shown here, hydraulic jets loosen the material around the pipe, while a dredge pump sucks the loosened material up to the surface and overboard through a discharge line.

Designed for use in extremely rough and unusually deep water is a huge lay barge that might be called a superbarge (fig. 6.35). It is 650 feet long, 140 feet wide, and 50 feet deep. The barge's centerline, elevated pipe ramp, and three pipe tensioners permit the laying of 80-foot length, double-jointed pipe in deep water, without the use of a pipe-laying pontoon.

The superbarge houses 350 people and can store as much as 20,000 tons of pipe. It has seven work stations for double-jointed pipe or nine work stations for 40-foot automatic or manual welding joints. It also includes a pipe-beveling station, two 125-ton capacity gantry cranes, twelve 60,000-pound anchors, and a heliport.

Figure 6.35. Designed for use in rough, deep water, this superbarge houses 350 people and can store as much as 20,000 tons of pipe. *(Courtesy of Brown & Root, Inc.)*

208

Coming to the forefront in offshore pipelining is the use of a semisubmersible lay barge, which operates in a manner similar to the semisubmersible drilling rig. The semisubmersible lay barge is designed to minimize the effects of wave and wind actions when operating in rough waters. For example, a semisubmersible barge crew continued to lay pipe in the North Sea during 35-foot waves and 70-mile-per-hour winds—an impossible task with a conventional lay barge. The stability comes from the submerged portion of the vessel, which lowers the center of gravity and steadies the vessel against heavy winds or high seas.

Reel barge

During the past several years, increasing use has been made of the reel pipe-laying barges (fig. 6.36). In the early development of the reel barge, pipe diameters were limited to small gathering line sizes of 1½ to 2 inches in diameter. Currently, lines of 8-inch diameter are being laid from the reels.

On reel barges the pipe is welded and spooled onto the giant reels at onshore facilities. To do this, pipe must be of sufficient flexibility to withstand reeling and unreeling without buckling or cracking.

The spooled line, ranging from several hundred feet to a couple of miles in length (depending on the pipe diameter), is unwound by moving the barge forward. The unreeled line is unspooled cleanly and in a straight path. Giant unspooling devices located at the rear of the barge, where the line extends to the water, keep the line straightened and unwrinkled. When one spool of line ends, the submerged line is held above the water surface while a new spool of line is joined by welding. Then the submerged line is dropped, and unspooling activity continues with the new line.

Figure 6.36. A giant spool unreels continuous lengths of line pipe from this reel lay barge.

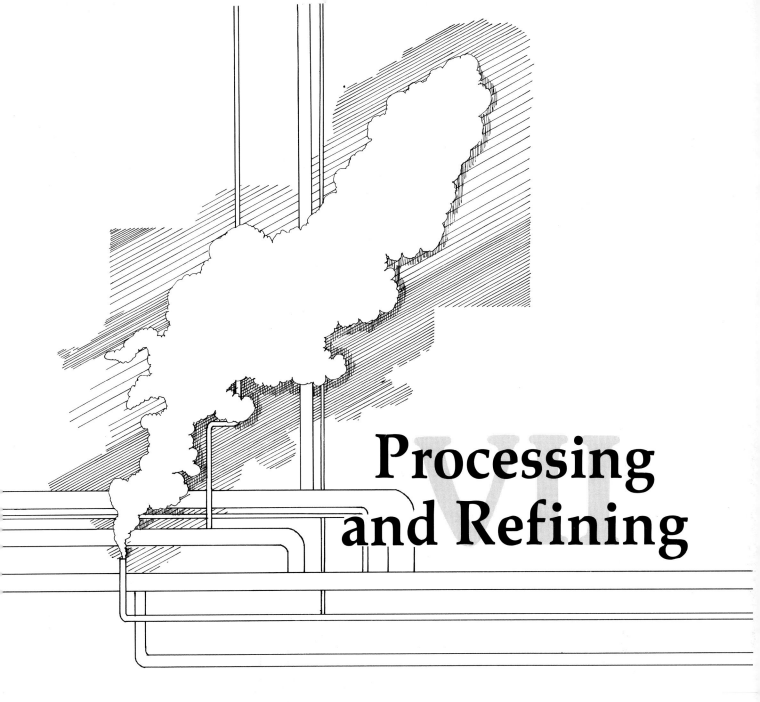

Processing and Refining

VII

C ollected crude oil and gas are of little use; the value of hydrocarbons lies in what is created from them: refined oils, solvents, fuels, and petrochemicals, which in turn are transformed into an almost limitless number of products ranging from fertilizer to plastic.

The refining world is a highly technical one that, to the layman, appears to be a strange setting of illuminated towers and structures at night (fig. 7.1) and an equally strange maze of pipes and tanks during the daytime (fig. 7.2). In reality, a refinery is an organized and coordinated arrangement of manufacturing processes designed to produce physical and chemical changes in crude oil and gas, resulting in salable products of the quality and quantity desired by the market (fig. 7.3). A refinery also includes the nonprocessing facilities, such as tankage for storage of crude oil and products, maintenance, and others, in order to maintain continuous operation.

Figure 7.1. A refinery unit lighted against the backdrop of a Louisiana sky at dusk *(Courtesy of Cities Service Company)*

Figure 7.2. Miles of pipe link the various units of a refinery. *(Courtesy of Cities Service Company)*

Figure 7.3. This Texas refinery has a capacity of 185,000 barrels per day.
(Courtesy of Coastal States Gas Corporation)

As crude oil comes from the well, it contains hydrocarbon compounds and other materials in relatively small quantities, such as oxygen, nitrogen, sulphur, salt, and water—plus trace amounts of certain metals. Therefore, crude oil must be converted through refining into products that will be marketable. The function of a refinery is to receive crude, break it down into various components, and blend the components into useful products.

Likewise, natural gas is a mixture of hydrocarbon gases, along with some impurities such as water and nonhydrocarbon gases (nitrogen, carbon dioxide, etc.). When raw, natural gas is withdrawn from the underground reservoirs, objectionable impurities are removed and desired products separated by various processing systems—both in the field and in gas processing plants.

Figure 7.4. This refinery in Louisiana is situated near a river and ship channel, where a portion of the facility's crude-oil feedstock is delivered by barge from gathering points along the inland waterways of southwest Louisiana and from offshore production in the Gulf of Mexico. *(Courtesy of Cities Service Company)*

CRUDE-OIL REFINING

Crude oil is petroleum as it comes from the oilwell or after extraneous substances such as water, gas, and minerals have been removed. It is oil in its natural or unprocessed state. It has weight or density that varies widely—sometimes so heavy and viscous it cannot be stirred with a stick and sometimes so light and thin it hardly seems to be a liquid. In color, it ranges from a clear yellow to opaque black. If a crude contains appreciable quantities of sulfur or sulfur compounds, it is called a *sour* crude; if it contains little or no sulfur, it is called a *sweet* crude.

Most crude oil falls into one of three classifications: asphalt-base, paraffin-base, or mixed-base. *Asphalt-base crude oil* contains little paraffin wax and a residue that is primarily asphaltic. Sulfur, oxygen, and nitrogen contents are often high. These crudes are particularly suitable for making high-quality gasoline and asphalt. *Paraffin-base crude* contains little or no asphaltic materials and is a good source of paraffin wax, quality motor lube oils, and high-grade kerosine. *Mixed-base crude* contains considerable amounts of both paraffin and asphalt. Virtually all products can be obtained from it, although at lower yields than from the other two classes.

Types of crude oil

Many processes are employed in the refining of crude oil. Some are quite complicated, and changes are made as researchers develop new methods of arranging the molecules of crude oil to produce more useful and profitable products. Processes are chosen, arranged, and interrelated according to the market the refinery serves and the products it manufactures.

Refining processes
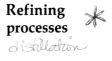

Refining starts with crude-oil fractionation, or separating crude into different parts, or fractions. This is usually accomplished by distillation. Resulting fractions include raw gasoline, kerosine, gas oil, lube, and other products not usually suitable for use as finished products.

Fractions are further treated and converted into salable products for use as fuel, lubrication, road paving materials, paints solvents, wax coatings, and various chemical compounds. A process called cracking is used to break down large chemical compounds into smaller compounds. Various treatments such as desalting remove impurities and improve properties of products.

Other processes build or reform new chemical compounds by chemical reactions. Major processes normally included in a modern refinery are distillation, cracking, polymerization, alkylation, sweetening or desulfurization, and desalting and dehydration.

214

Distillation   Such products as raw gasoline, diesel oil, asphalt, and fuel oil are retrieved from the crude oil by means of distillation. This separation process is quite simple in principle and may be compared to the process of turning water into steam in a teakettle. When steam cools, it returns to its former liquid state. Crude stills, or distillation units, that make up a large part of a refinery may be visualized as giant teakettles. Crude oil piped in is heated, and a portion turns into a vapor. This heating process separates the many components comprising crude oil into groups having similar boiling points. When the vapor condenses, the various groups having different boiling points are condensed separately into distillates, which in turn can be used in their new state or blended with other materials to make a useful product. The portion of the crude that does not vaporize in the stills, called *residuum*, may be used as fuel oil or further processed into products more in demand.

Cracking   Cracking processes break down the heavier hydrocarbon molecules into the lighter gasoline and distillate range products. The heavier fuel-oil and gas-oil distillate fractions are converted to the more valuable gasoline and light distillate stocks. Two principal types of cracking are thermal and catalytic. *Thermal cracking* uses heat and pressure to effect the conversion of the larger molecules into smaller ones. *Catalytic cracking* makes use of a catalyst. A catalyst is a substance that makes the conversion take place at less severe conditions of pressure (fig. 7.5). Temperatures used are essentially the same in both thermal and catalytic cracking.

Figure 7.5. Three catalytic cracking units perform a vital process in separating the crude-oil stream into components that will eventually become finished petroleum products. *(Courtesy of Cities Service Company)*

Reforming uses catalysts and heat to rearrange hydrocarbon molecules *without* changing their composition. Catalytic reforming units, or reformers, are used to convert petroleum naphtha into more volatile products of higher octane. The process is used for upgrading the octane of gasoline, converting naphtha to liquefied petroleum gas, and producing aromatic hydrocarbons—a feedstock for explosives, detergents, plastics, and other petrochemical products. The process actually uses a number of different reactions, such as isomerization, hydrocracking, polymerization, and dehydrogenation.

Reforming

In a sense, polymerization is the opposite of cracking; that is, certain hydrocarbon molecules lighter than gasoline are combined with similar molecules to produce a high-octane gasoline blending stock. In both thermal and catalytic polymerization processes, the reaction is effected through high temperatures and pressures. However, as in the cracking process, the use of a catalyst allows the process to proceed at less severe conditions of temperature and pressure.

Polymerization

Alkylation is similar to polymerization in that light hydrocarbon molecules are combined to form a heavier molecule—usually in the gasoline range. The processes differ in that the alkylation process combines dissimilar molecules. The gasoline product usually is of a high-octane quality and is quite important in the blending of aviation gasoline.

Alkylation

Crude oil and products contain some sulfur compounds such as hydrogen sulfide, mercaptans, sulfides, and disulfides. Various processes are used to desulfurize products, depending on the type of sulfur present and the desired quality of the end product.

Sweetening or desulfurization

Many processes are used for removing both salt and water from crude oil. Crude oil is heated, an emulsion breaker is added, and the resultant mass is settled or filtered to remove the salt and water from the oil.

Desalting and dehydration

Several other processes in a refinery deserve mention. These include (1) the treating of oils with heat and solvents to manufacture wax, (2) the treating of heavy distillate oils so that they are useful for lubricating, (3) the mixing of various petroleum components with purchased ingredients to make grease for lubricating purposes, and (4) the manufacture or blending of various products in the field of petrochemicals to produce synthetic rubber, plastics, pharmaceuticals, insecticides, fungicides, fertilizers, and the like.

Other processes

GAS PROCESSING

As late as the 1930s, natural gas was flared and blown to the air in large volumes. When gas accompanied crude oil, the gas had to find a market nearby or be flared. With the advent of gas pipelines (commonly called transmission lines), gas processing facilities, and conservation practices, oilwell gas production became a thriving industry.

The facilities normally operated in the handling of gas in the field are those required to condition the gas to make it marketable—the removal of impurities, water, and excess hydrocarbon liquids and the control of delivery pressure. The last operation involves the use of compressors and pressure-reducing regulators.

Gas processing systems

Natural gas processing plants (fig. 7.6) are usually designed to remove certain valuable products (natural gasoline, butane, propane, ethane, and even methane) over and above those needed to make the gas marketable. Plants may also be designed to recover elemental sulfur from the hydrogen sulfide gas removed from wellhead gas. Another function of plants is to separate the liquid hydrocarbons recovered into various mixtures or pure products by the use of fractionating columns. Plants nearly always incorporate in

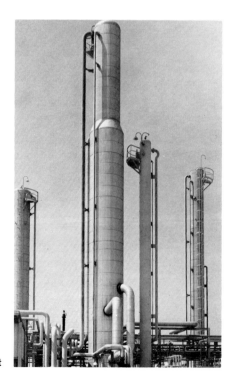

Figure 7.6. A gas processing plant

their processes many of the functions ordinarily performed by field facilities, such as dehydration and hydrogen sulfide removal. Hydrocarbons of primary concern in gas processing operations are methane, ethane, propane, isobutane, normal butane, isopentane, normal pentane, hexane, heptane, octane, nonane, and decane—listed from lightest to heaviest. Common plant processes include oil absorption, fractionation, dehydration, and cryogenic processing.

Oil absorption plants are used for the removal of hydrocarbon products from natural gas. Three primary processing systems in an oil absorption plant are recovery, rejection, and separation (fig. 7.7). Products are recovered or removed from the inlet gas in the recovery system by a combination of refrigeration and oil absorption. Some methane is also recovered with the product, and current specifications allow very little methane. The second processing system rejects the methane from the product stream, leaving only product and absorption oil, which are separated in the third system.

Oil absorption

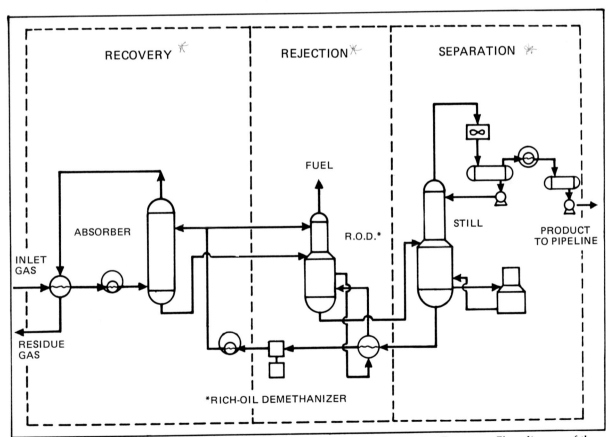

Figure 7.7. Flow diagram of three primary processing systems in an oil absorption plant

Fractionation

A system or process called fractionation is used to separate the mixture of products into individual products for sale (fig. 7.8). Fractionation is possible when the two products to be separated have different boiling points. The usual order is to remove the lighter product first. Hydrocarbon components normally processed in a fractionation plant are ethane, propane, isobutane, normal butane, pentanes, and natural gasoline, listed in the order of decreasing volatility (readily vaporizable at a relatively low temperature). Essential parts of a fractionation system are the tower condenser, reboiler, and reflux equipment (fig. 7.9). Getting the necessary vapor and liquid contact requires a large number of trays in the tower, a lot of heat input by the reboiler, and heat removal by the reflux and condenser. Fractionators are usually named for the overhead, or top, product. Therefore, a deethanizer implies that the top product is ethane, a depropanizer indicates that the top product is propane, and so on.

Dehydration

All hydrocarbon fluids can retain some water. Hydrates will form if a gas or liquid containing free water is cooled below its hydrate temperature. Hydrates are solid compounds that form as crystals and resemble snow in appearance. They are created by a reaction of natural gas with water. To avoid free-water problems that cause freezing and the formation of hydrates, a dehydration process is used. Dehydration is the removal of water from a substance and may be accomplished by one of two methods: (1) contact of the gas with glycol, which is a liquid (fig. 7.10), or (2) dry-bed dehydration, an adsorption process using a solid (fig. 7.11).

Figure 7.8. At this natural gas liquids fractionation center, mixed liquid streams enter the refinery and are fractionated into natural gasoline, normal butane, isobutane, propane, and ethane. *(Courtesy of Cities Service Company)*

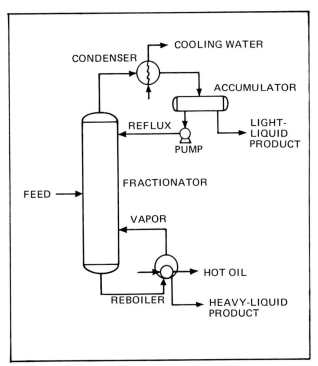

Figure 7.9. Fractionation system

Figure 7.10. Arrows indicate the injection points for introducing glycol or methanol to prevent hydrate formation at a point in the flow stream.

Figure 7.11. Dry-bed dehydration system

Cryogenic processing

Cryogenic processing requires the proper combination of pressure and temperature to achieve the desired product recovery. Since temperatures of –50°F or lower are required for cryogenic processing of natural gas, specialized equipment and techniques are used. Contaminants such as salt water, wax, dirt, scale, iron sulfide, and oil carried over from wellhead separators and compressors must be removed because they cause exchanger fouling and flow stoppage. Cryogenic processing requires specialized core heat exchangers, construction materials that have large thermal expansion properties, cold boxes that insulate the processing equipment, and control valves and pumps with extended shafts so they can be operated deep inside the insulation of the cold box with motor and works external.

Treating processes

Many natural gases must be treated; that is, sulfur compounds and carbon dioxide (CO_2) must be removed. The sulfur compound found in largest quantities in natural gas is hydrogen sulfide (H_2S). Both H_2S and CO_2 are called acid gases, and their removal is often called *sweetening*. Sour gases are those having high concentrations of sulfur compounds.

Many commercial gas-treating processes are used in the industry; however, there are two general classifications: (1) absorption and (2) adsorption. In absorption processes, the gas stream contacts a liquid that selectively removes acid gases. In some absorption processes the gases are physically dissolved in the liquid, and the liquid is regenerated so the absorbed acid gases flash out of the liquid. In other absorption processes, the acid gases react chemically with the liquid, and heat is used to regenerate the liquid and drive off the gases.

In an adsorption process, generally called a dry-bed unit, the sour-gas stream contacts a solid adsorbent that selectively removes the sulfur compounds and/or carbon dioxide. The adsorbent material is then regenerated with heat or by lowering the pressure.

PETROCHEMICALS

Although most petroleum products are used as energy sources, such as gasoline for cars, fuel oil for boats and ships, and natural gas for heating and fuel, petroleum is also a major component in the manufacture of petrochemicals (fig. 7.12). A petrochemical is a pure chemical substance produced commercially from petroleum or natural gas by processors handling petroleum raw materials. Consequently, many petrochemical plants are integral parts of large refining complexes and often are subsidiaries of major oil companies.

Figure 7.12. This olefins manufacturing complex produces 1.2 million metric tons per year of ethylene plus large quantities of propylene and other petrochemical co-products. *(Courtesy of ARCO Chemical Company)*

Three groups of petrochemicals, based on chemical composition and structure, are aliphatic, aromatic, and inorganic. *Aliphatic* petrochemicals are organic compounds—that is, they contain carbon. Included in this group are ethylene, polyethylene, styrene, and ethyl alcohol. The major feedstocks, or raw materials, for this group are methane, ethane, propane, and butane. *Aromatic* petrochemicals are also organic compounds but contain or are derived from the basic benzene ring of six carbon atoms. Benzene, toluene, and xylene are important sources of aromatic petrochemicals. *Inorganic* petrochemicals do not contain carbon atoms in compounds. Typical are sulfur, ammonia, and carbon black.

Basic types of petrochemicals

Organic chemical reactions used in the manufacture of petrochemicals are unlimited as are the equipment and power necessary to effect these processes (fig. 7.13). More and better processes are being developed continuously. Some of the major processes in use today are the following:

alkylation—addition of alkyl;
aromatization—converting paraffins to aromatics;
chlorination—addition or substitution of chlorine;
dehydration—removing water;
dehydrogenation—removing hydrogen;
hydration—combining with water;
hydrogenation—adding hydrogen;
hydrolysis—splitting compound with water;
oxidation—combining with oxygen; and
polymerization—combining small molecules into larger ones.

Manufacturing processes

Figure 7.13. This 20,000-horsepower centrifugal compressor, driven by a high-pressure steam turbine, is an example of the huge yet precise mechanical equipment required to handle process streams in a modern petrochemical plant. *(Courtesy of ARCO Chemical Company)*

Figure 7.14. A host of finished products are made with the plastics manufactured at a petrochemical plant.

Figure 7.15. By means of elaborate instruments, a process technician can tell by a glance at a meter or chart what temperature or pressure is being applied in any section of a petrochemical unit, adjusting those conditions by merely touching a switch or turning a dial.

The basic job of most petrochemical plants is to turn a petroleum derivative into feedstocks that will ultimately be used in the manufacture of a host of other products, ranging from ammonia to the plastic bottle containing it. Since the number of petrochemicals manufactured ranges in the thousands, each petrochemical plant has different processes, procedures, facilities, and auxiliary operations. To get an insight into a petrochemical plant, consider the operation of Tex-Chem, a hypothetical petrochemical plant that manufactures two basic plastics—polyethylene and polypropylene.

Situated in the heart of oil country where miles of pipelines crisscross underground and barges ply the waterways, Tex-Chem uses several basic raw materials as its feedstocks. All are derived from petroleum or natural-gas recovery and, as a result of today's petrochemical technology, are used in the manufacture of thousands of synthetic materials.

From these feedstocks, the plant manufactures polyethylene and polypropylene, which are used in various appliance and automotive parts, moldings, battery cases, luggage, bottles, plastic toys, transparent food wrappers, plastic containers, and a wide range of construction materials (fig. 7.14).

The plant operates 24 hours a day, seven days a week. Although the chemical processes themselves are complex, they involve the application of familiar principles: controlled temperature, pressure, and time and sometimes the presence of a catalyst and a solvent. All operations take place in a labyrinth of pipes, valves, silos, and towers, controlled by elaborate instruments and monitored by trained technicians (fig. 7.15). Basically, the plant is divided into three elements: the olefins units, the polymer units, and the supporting facilities.

Olefins units

The primary job of the olefins units is to provide ethylene and propylene for the polymer units (polyethylene and polypropylene units), as well as for sale to other chemical or plastic producers. The olefins units, sometimes referred to as a petrochemical refinery because of their wide range of products, also produce butadiene, butenes, hydrogen, and aromatics for use in the manufacture of other chemicals or gasoline production. These co-products are sold to other chemical producers or used as feedstocks for other plants operated by the Tex-Chem company.

Some of the processes involved are steam cracking of hydrocarbons, noble metal catalytic conversion of acetylenes, cryogenic separation of hydrogen, and selective adsorption using molecular sieves. Input consists of both liquid distillates, such as natural gasoline and virgin naphtha, and liquefied ethane and propane gases.

224

Polymer units

The polymerization of propylene and ethylene takes place in the polymer units of the plant. The polypropylene and polyethylene processes are catalytic ones with the polymerization reaction carried out in a liquid solvent. Polymer properties depend on the length of the polymer chain, which is controlled by the hydrogen concentration in the reactor. Following polymerization, the product is removed from the reactor and processed through a purification facility for removal of catalyst residue and separation of the solvent. The powdered product is then conveyed in a pneumatic conveyor to the finishing area where additives are blended with powder and the mixture is processed through an extruder to produce the pelleted product (fig. 7.16).

Figure 7.16. Polypropylene is extruded into pellets about the size of a BB in its finished form.

Supporting facilities

Extensive laboratory testing is conducted throughout the process to maintain quality control (fig. 7.17). Polyethylene and polypropylene pellets are checked for proper content and consistency. If product specifications are met, the pellets are prepared for shipping (fig. 7.18).

Figure 7.17. Laboratory analysts run extensive tests on raw materials, process stream, and finished products to assure that quality is being maintained.

Figure 7.18. Polypropylene pellets are sacked or put in cardboard boxes for trucking to other locations.

Conservation of energy, air, and water are reflected in the plant's operation. The water used to cool the process units is purified by the plant's water-treatment facilities and reused (fig. 7.19). Environmental-oriented planning controls air pollution, allowing only steam to rise from the plant's cooling towers and units. The steam is odorless, contains no contaminants, and rapidly disperses into the atmosphere. The intermittent discharge of waste hydrocarbon gas from the process units—a potential source of air pollution—is handled with a flare system that burns the waste hydrocarbons in tall, derricklike structures. Process units are designed to make full use of the energy consumed, and, in many instances, energy-producing hydrocarbons are created as by-products, recovered, and used as fuel.

Companion plant

Linked closely with the operation of this Tex-Chem plant is another plant located nearby. Using feedstocks from plant No. 1, Tex-Chem's plant No. 2 produces specialty chemicals and petrochemical intermediates for the manufacture of other products. Some of these chemicals and their ultimate use in products of all kinds are shown in table 7.1.

Table 7.1
Some Petrochemicals and Their Uses

Feedstock	Petrochemical	Typical Final Products
Styrene	Polystyrene	Cups and glasses, phonograph records, radio and TV cabinets, furniture, luggage, telephones, ice chests, lighting fixtures
Paraxylene	Terephthalic acid (PTA), dimethyl terephthalate (DMT)	Polyester fibers used to make wearing apparel, tire cords; polyester film used to make electronic recording tape, photographic film, cooking pouches, specialty packaging items
Metaxylene	Isophthalic acid (IPA)	Fiberglass-reenforced auto bodies, surf boards, snowmobile housings, outboard motor covers, cooling fans, vaulting poles, many paints and coatings.
Propylene	Polypropylene	Appliance parts, bottles, safety helmets, disposable syringes, battery cases, construction materials, feed bags, carpet backing

Figure 7.19. In the aeration basin of the plant's water treatment facilities, millions of tiny bacteria literally eat the hydrocarbon waste in the water, making the water leaving the plant more pure than that entering the plant.

Petroleum Marketing

b y the very nature of its success in the competitive industrial market, petroleum has evolved into an international market commodity. Also contributing to its international character is the fact that petroleum is not generally found where it is most extensively used. Early centers of industrialism were founded around areas rich in coal and iron ore. By chance, petroleum in the twentieth century has not been produced in large quantities close to heavily industrialized areas.

Today, countries are defined as producer and/or consumer countries. This distinction has helped make the oil industry a complex and fascinating market that vastly influences relationships between countries. Petroleum raw materials and products are, in fact, the largest and most influential commodities selling in the world today.

The discovery of petroleum and the development of its useful products have made possible a giant leap in the living conditions of mankind. Used explosively in combination with air, petroleum has made twentieth-century man mobile on land, on sea, and in the air. Man has been able to more effectively heat, light, and cool his environment with the electricity and gas made available by petroleum. Agricultural and manufacturing processes have greatly expanded and improved because of the refinement of produced hydrocarbons. As more valuable petroleum products have been developed and its availability has lessened, the worldwide push to search for hydrocarbons and explore their product potential has intensified.

Changing needs

Petroleum was first valued in the latter part of the nineteenth century for its potential as a lighting fuel in the form of kerosine. Since then, it has widened its market at a rapid rate. With the advent of the automobile, the need for internal-combustion engine fuel developed, and less of the crude-oil cut was designated for kerosine and more for the products that would blend into gasoline. (A *cut* is a fraction of petroleum separated in the course of a process.) Up until 1912, the gasoline sold was only that originally in the crude or that condensed from natural gas. With the advent of the refining process called cracking, more gasoline per barrel of crude could be produced, and that gasoline had less tendency to knock than straight-run gasoline from the distilling process.

As the octane race intensified, a new refinery process was developed: that of reforming—both thermal and catalytic reforming. Two other processes, polymerization and alkylation, helped in the effort over this century to produce a higher percentage of gasoline out of the crude barrel, with an ever higher octane rating. Thus, the need for kerosine changed to a need for gasoline, creating enormous challenges in the distillation and marketing of the crude oil barrel.

Marketing entities

To meet the new needs of the industry, four distinct entities developed in the petroleum marketing industry: the U.S. Majors, the U.S. Internationals, the European Internationals, and the national oil companies of developing nations.

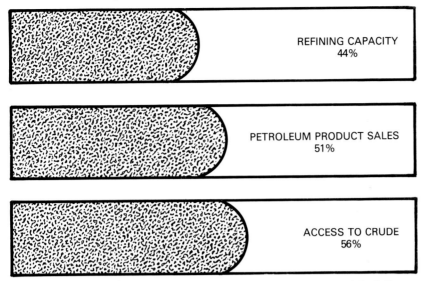

REFINING CAPACITY
44%

PETROLEUM PRODUCT SALES
51%

ACCESS TO CRUDE
56%

Statistics from Joe D. Fischer and Constantine Fliakos, *British Petroleum: A Basic Report* (New York: Drexel Burnham Lambert, Inc. 1978), p. 30.

Figure 8.1. The Majors' involvement in the noncommunist World oil industry

The Majors

The kerosine market of the late nineteenth century was characterized by surpluses and shortages. In the midst of this confusion, one man took over—John D. Rockefeller, president of Standard Oil Company. The company was famous for getting more kerosine from a barrel of crude than any of the other proliferating refineries. Rockefeller bought out many of the rival refineries until he owned 90 percent of the American refinery capacity. He was soon able to control also the distribution and marketing end of the business. In 1911, the U.S. Supreme Court ordered the breakup of Standard Oil into separate entities.

Three of the companies emerging out of Standard Oil eventually became part of the seven *Majors.* These seven companies, until recently, controlled a huge percentage of the development, production, refining, transport, and marketing of the international oil industry. The seven Majors are Exxon, Chevron, Mobil Oil, Gulf Oil, Texaco, Royal Dutch/Shell, and British Petroleum. Five of these companies are based in the United States; and one, Royal Dutch/Shell, has a large percentage of its holdings in the U.S. The world's oil industry is now experiencing radical changes in its structure; however, the Majors continue to control about half of the world's development, refining, and marketing (fig. 8.1).

U.S. Internationals

Another structural entity of the petroleum marketing world is often referred to as the *U.S. Internationals.* These companies, smaller than the Majors, began to seek oil markets abroad after World War II. The companies expanded predominantly in Western Europe. Examples of the U.S. International group are Amoco, Continental Oil, Atlantic Richfield, Sun Oil, Phillips, and Marathon Oil. With both this level of industry and that of the Majors operational in the United States, the marketing structure of the oil industry can be defined as an *oligopoly*, a market in which each of a few producers affects but does not control the market. (Also, legislation has ensured the continued existence of numerous small-scale independent companies in the U.S.)

The U.S. International oil companies chose to expand their interests abroad during the late 1940s and early 1950s. The post-war market was one of demand; and state regulatory bodies in the U.S., such as the Texas Railroad Commission, were limiting through proration policies the amount of petroleum that could be extracted. Those policies were based on U.S. availability and demand. The oil abroad cost less to produce and seemed limitless at that time. The U.S. domestic oil industry and other concerned groups protested as the Internationals increased their importing operations into the U.S.

The Majors responded more or less to government requests for voluntary cutbacks in imports. But most of the smaller Internationals, having recently invested abroad, did not cut back. In 1959, President Eisenhower introduced mandatory oil quotas on both crude oil and oil products. The quotas, set at a percentage of the U.S. total use of oil, helped control the rate of oil imports.

Some companies, which had invested heavily abroad, decided to search for markets in other parts of the world. The oil that thus became available on the world market created a glut and acted to upset the previous orderly marketing situation. World prices fell, and U.S. companies abroad reduced payments to host countries for their crude. This event and others would soon lead to the formation of the Organization of Petroleum Exporting Countries (OPEC).

European Internationals

Before dealing with the national companies of the developing nations, one other influential entity in the worldwide marketing structure needs definition. France, Belgium, and Italy now have oil companies comparable in size to the U.S. Internationals. They are Compagnie Française des Pétroles, the Belgian Petrofina Company, and Ente Nazionale Idrocarburi in Italy.

Other countries, of course, figure in the international market. Japan, with its high demand, has been a very special market for international companies. The USSR has been, and China is fast becoming, a major producing and consuming area. Since relatively little is documented regarding Russian and Chinese reserves, production, and consumption, most traditional marketing statistics have been limited to the noncommunist world.

The fourth entity in the industry's structure—national oil companies—is closely linked to the development of OPEC:

> By 1960, 45 percent of the world's oil outside the USA and USSR was produced in the Middle East, and over 50 percent of that internationally traded was exported from that area.[1]

Concession agreements had allowed international companies to come into undeveloped countries to develop and export oil and gas. Profits were usually shared on a 50-50 basis between the countries that owned the oil and the companies that produced it. The profits were based on "posted prices" published at levels decided on by the participating companies. Posted prices were dropped after the United States imposed import quotas. The closure of the Suez Canal in 1956–57 also affected the situation. In August, 1960, posted prices were reduced in the Middle East.

In September, 1960, OPEC was formed. As the 60s progressed, worldwide demand could only be met by sizable increases in imports from OPEC countries. National companies gradually participated more and more in the control of their indigenous resources. "Participation" meant increased ownership in production activities and financial responsibility for exploration development. The international oil companies continued to varying degrees to control refining and marketing of the countries' petroleum.

The Arab-Israeli war (1973–1974) resulted in an oil embargo by the Arab countries against the U.S. for its support of Israel. Effective ownership of production was transferred to local governments or their national oil companies. By the end of 1973, oil prices had increased nearly fivefold. President Nixon quickly instigated a push for greater U.S. independence from petroleum imports in the form of "Project Energy Independence 1980." National oil companies in the Middle East and in other developing nations sought greater downstream involvement by developing refinery and marketing operations. And the world as a whole ended the 1970s with its marketing balance of power greatly altered.

In effect, the higher prices decreed by OPEC worked as a tax levied on oil-importing nations. Increased oil prices aggravated inflationary conditions that affected direct consumption of oil and caused higher production costs in all sectors. Especially affected in the world economy were the less developed countries. Many experts predicted that the anticipated shift of financial resources would prove disastrous to the world economy.

However, the most dire predictions failed to materialize for several reasons. OPEC countries suffered inflationary bottlenecks also, and an unexpectedly high rate of increase in OPEC imports occurred. The United States has succeeded to an extent in making

1. Joel D. Fischer and Constantine D. Fliakos, *British Petroleum: A Basic Report* (New York: Drexel Burnham Lambert, Inc., 1978), p. 19.

itself more energy self-sufficient through conservation efforts, more oil exploration, greater utilization of natural gas, and more efforts to turn to new sources of energy. In 1975, the major oil companies still controlled 44 percent of worldwide marketing.[2] Sophisticated technical knowledge and supply planning, covering total systems from exploration to retail sales, give the major oil companies both economies of scale and integration in meeting the needs of the marketplace.

Whether the world petroleum market today can be called an oligopoly is open to question. OPEC had 70 percent of the proved oil reserves of the noncommunist world in 1977.[3] How the OPEC countries will use these reserves to control prices leads to difficulties for planners trying to construct models for the international petroleum market. In theoretical marketing terms, should these models be based on competitive structures or monopolistic structures? Although OPEC may often seem to act as a cartel, the different countries involved have yet to agree on their production totals. Oil prices are determined at this time mainly by the leadership of Saudi Arabia with its huge reserves. There is general agreement that the price for Saudi light crude functions as the market price. And, with its current trend towards deregulation of price, the U.S. is allowing its crude prices to rise toward the world market price.

FUNCTIONS OF MARKETING

Responsibilities of a marketing department in an oil company or a marketing company in the petroleum industry may include sales, financial management, research and planning, distribution, and advertising. The detail and depth at which these objectives are pursued depends, of course, on the nature of the company being served. A petroleum broker, who buys and sells only products, may not need a long-term planner to predict the need for crude in five years. That particular kind of company may also not need advertising but, instead, may rely on word-of-mouth reputation.

A distinction needs to be made between the marketing methods of a *vertically integrated* oil company and that of an *independent marketer*. A company that is large enough to be involved in all aspects of the oil industry is referred to as being vertically integrated. Its marketing practices will be integrated within the company's exploration, drilling, production, refining, transporting, and distribution activities. Such a company will sell some or all of its automotive products at a service station bearing the company emblem, thereby carrying its petroleum from the reservoir to the retail outlet.

2. *Our Magnificent Earth: A Rand McNally Atlas of Earth Resources* (New York: Rand McNally & Co., 1979), p. 2.18.
3. *Our Magnificent Earth*, p. 2.14.

Figure 8.2. A broker often handles transactions without leaving his office.

Independent marketers, on the other hand, will function at one of several levels in the marketing chain. They will buy *bulk*—either the overstock of name brand refiners or products from independent refineries. They may be brokers who buy and sell mostly on paper (fig. 8.2), or they may arrange to take delivery of their requirements. They often *spot buy,* or purchase spontaneously in accord with the momentary market rather than according to long-range planning. Or, independent marketers may have contractual agreements for specified time periods with their suppliers. An independent marketer may also be engaged in storage, transporting, and distribution.

In any marketing concern, sales are the first consideration, although purchases of raw materials and feedstocks, as well as trades, also affect operations. Through planning, long-range and short-term, running the selling operation at the highest volume of profit becomes the ultimate goal.

Planning and research

Balancing supply and demand is one of the main objectives of marketing research. Today, computers are often instrumental in this role. Analyzing and predicting the petroleum market is a complex task; many factors are at stake. The worldwide supply of petroleum has been found to be limited at a time when the planet's way of life is committed to using those resources. The coming and gradual changeover to other fuel sources must be taken into account by any researcher.

Related to the realization of the limits of petroleum resources is an attitude toward conservation on the part of consumers and manufacturers. Users of petroleum and its products are being asked, and in some cases forced, to slow down. Many nations feel that an orderly changeover to other fuels can be accomplished more easily if petroleum is sensibly conserved and therefore used at a slower rate in the coming decades. But, predicting this future rate in the face of the expected demand for continually improving quality of life and the worldwide growth in population is a difficult task for a planner.

Because of its scarcity, petroleum is often involved in international skirmishes. A border war in the Middle East can immediately influence the price of oil in Houston. The planner must be flexible enough to take into consideration the unpredictable political implications of the industry. Technology also is changing at such a rapid rate that a petroleum product seemingly irreplaceable today may become obsolete tomorrow. Researchers must keep themselves abreast of current and possible future technological breakthroughs. Along with this possibility, the researcher must contemplate the rising cost of energy. The exploration and development of the two new major oil areas discovered in the 1960s—the North Sea and Alaska—have cost ten to twenty times as much as developing similar fields in the Middle East.[4] These sorts of changes, though difficult to predict, must figure constantly into any petroleum planner's scenario.

Marketing time periods

Marketing planners research for three different time periods—the present, the near future, and the more distant future. Policies governing *present* marketing are constantly analyzed for effectiveness. The size of the current market, which brands are selling, and where retail distribution is occurring can all be measured. Seasonal factors must be accounted for, since gasoline sells more during the summer vacation months, and heating fuels are needed during the winter months. Research within a company can determine how well its advertising and public relations efforts are working. Consumer behavior must be watched for changing preferences that might indicate simple inclination or greater response to a competitor.

4. Fischer and Fliakos, p. 20.

The *near future* is usually defined in the marketing world as the next three years. This phase of research usually involves pretesting of new products, services, methods, or publicity. A distinction is made between pretesting and test marketing. *Pretesting* is done under simulated market conditions, and *test marketing* is conducted in the real conditions of the ever-changing market. Pretesting is usually used for choosing between alternatives.

In order to predict the *more distant future,* a combination of human imagination and utilization of scientific prediction methods is required. The elements of the future are often present in society and can be used along with historical data to predict coming patterns with some accuracy. Demographic indicators such as population numbers, geographical structure, size of families, and educational and financial levels can be fed into machines for predictions of future consumer trends. Marketing research hopefully reduces the risk of decision making for the future; but, with the rapid acceleration of change in our technological world, sound and instant human judgment will always be needed in petroleum marketing.

Supply and demand

Once the consumer market is assessed, the next and more encompassing role of the planner is to match marketing requirements with resources—in other words, to balance supply and demand. In the past, supply has been able to grow with demand, but a time may be coming in the petroleum market when supply will dictate demand. Along with this problem, a marketing plan must embrace the considerations of possible sources of crude, refinery capacity, and availability of shipping and pipelining. With massive data input, the plan must be able to predict with some accuracy a balance between input and output of an entire system. In a large oil company, meshing together all activities into an efficient and profitable operation becomes quite a task.

Computer models

Sophisticated linear programming techniques run on computers are used to evaluate the many options available. Various mathematical models generate solutions from computerized data. Supply planners must then decide upon the practicality of the various programs, because the most economical future solution is not always the most desirable in terms of current conditions.

An example of such planning is the mathematical model used by the authors of the National Energy Plan (1977) to predict energy futures. This model, referred to as Project Independence Energy Systems (PIES), was used to answer questions similar to those a marketing planner might ask. Two types of information were recorded on reels of magnetic tape that could be fed into a computer. One set of tapes held the *program,* describing the expected relationships among factors involved in the energy system. For instance: how much more oil would be found in the United States in response to a given effort to find it; what increase in the price of petroleum products would occur if total deregulation were allowed. The second set of tapes held the actual data from recent years relevant to the relationships set up in the first set of tapes. Examples of these data would be the number of drilling rigs used in given years; the amount of oil found annually; recent world crude prices; domestic petroleum products prices, and so forth. (These examples comprise only a very few of the relationships and data fed into the PIES mathematical model.)

When such tapes are inserted into appropriate computers, the numerical values in the second set of tapes are entered into the mathematical relationships established by the first set of tapes. After the computers perform their calculations, they print out tables of figures that help planners make predictions—in the case of PIES, predictions about energy futures. In the case of marketing models, the predictions would involve pricing, size of markets, inclination of future consumers, and other patterns influencing supply and demand.

Crude acquisition

Valid considerations for a petroleum planner concerning crude acquisition will include not only the immediate oil needs indicated by marketing research, but also the need to build up or deplete stocks for future periods. The marketing flexibility provided by an oil company's owning storage and transportation facilities becomes crucial at this point. Usually, a margin of shipping capacity is left to be acquired by spot buying. Having storage tanks and shipping facilities waiting makes this kind of action possible.

The different grades and quantities of crude that will be available at any one time must also figure into a broad plan. A marketing company may choose to buy from another company or abroad rather than use its own crude, even when the company is also a producing concern. Or it may choose to trade for the various qualities of crude demanded by the dictates of its own predicted market.

The availability of future crude, of course, depends on worldwide reserves and the ability of future technology to extract it at a price less than the worth of the energy produced.

> Although there are abundant known reserves in the Middle East (45 times as great as present annual production) and Africa (26 times present annual production), the position elsewhere is not so satisfactory.[5]

A planning researcher must have reliable worldwide statistics programmed into his machines. He will either keep abreast of current news and scientific journals or he will employ a consulting

5. *Our Magnificent Earth*, p. 2.17.

Table 8.1
Typical Marketing Information

Industry Scoreboard 10/6	Latest week 9-26-80	Change from Week before*		Change from Year ago		% change Year ago
Demand, 1,000 b/d: (4-week avg.)						
Motor gasoline	6,583	—	39	—	424	— 6.1
Middle distillates	2,535	+	29	—	64	— 2.5
Jet fuel	983	—	74	—	153	—13.5
Residual	2,157	—	19	—	306	—12.4
Other products	3,829	—	116	—	71	— 1.8
Total demand	16,087	—	219	—	1,018	— 6.0
Supply, 1,000 b/d: (4-week avg.)						
Crude production	8,679	—	7	+	109	+ 1.3
Crude imports	5,024	—	18	—	1,261	—20.1
Product imports	1,406	—	58	—	258	—15.5
Crude runs to stills	13,321	+	32	—	1,210	— 8.3
Stocks, 1,000 bbl:						
Crude	391,499	+	2,903	+	72,372	+22.7
Motor gasoline	260,470	—	1,404	+	30,683	+13.4
Middle distillates	247,507	—	857	+	4,541	+ 1.9
Jet fuel	42,100	+	1,314	+	9,412	+28.8
Residual	92,264	+	597	+	1,876	+ 2.1
Drilling: (4-week avg.)						
Rotary rigs	3,107	+	17	+	803	+34.9

*Based on revised figures

SOURCE: *Oil & Gas Journal Newsletter,* October 6, 1980.

service to do so for him. Commonly used marketing reports are *Platt's Oilgram Price Report* and *The Lundberg Letter.* Such services help not only with availability, but with pricing. Oil companies will frequently have researchers who watch and contribute to government legislation affecting availability and pricing. Information such as that shown in table 8.1 is essential knowledge for a marketing planner trying to construct a valid program of supply and demand.

Refinery capacity

Planning for refinery capacity in the future is complicated by the fact that it takes about five years from the time of decision to bring a major new refining plant on stream. The estimated profitable output over the life of the refinery must justify the amount of capital required to invest in a new plant. Smaller refining investment projects may include increased dock facilities, energy conservation facilities, or new storage areas.

Transportation

Having available ocean-going vessels ready to pick up and deliver the proper qualities of crude and selection of products is another task of planners. Cost per unit of product declines as more volume is carried, and crude oil can now be shipped in cargoes of half-million tons. A tanker that carries more than 150,000 tons is referred to as a *very large crude carrier* (VLCC). Products are characteristically shipped in smaller tankers. A planner, or scheduler, of transportation must select carriers, make sure they are at the proper loading points, monitor crude and product stocks to have them ready for loading, and choose appropriate routings.

Transportation timing and coordination may be affected by market fluctuations, weather, vessel engine trouble, or political upsets. Cargoes can neither be loaded before they are available nor allowed to accrue so much that refinery or process throughput has to be stopped because of lack of storage space. Details must be considered such as a ship's shape and its capacity. One ship might require more depth of water while another a longer jetty for docking and loading. Barges are used to transport crude and products through intercoastal canals (fig. 8.3). Product ships may carry more than one type of cargo, and contamination must be avoided. Often the cargoes are unloaded at different destinations; therefore, the ship must be loaded so that the trim is not upset when the first product is discharged. Since VLCCs are often too large to enter ports, *entrepot* oil ports and methods of discharging at sea have been developed.

Distribution

Another function of marketing is distribution. The task of delivering petroleum products from processing plants and refineries to the final consumers is complex and often costly. The combined costs of product storage and handling, transportation, and delivery can add up to more than half the total operating costs of a marketing department. The fewer handling or reloading operations done per trip, the lower the total cost will be.

Natural gas

In the case of natural gas, transcontinental pipelines carry the marketable product from producing areas to urban consumers. Local distribution companies, mostly privately owned, buy gas from the pipelines and make it available to consumers in homes, apartments, businesses, and sometimes industry. In order to perform this service, local companies operate an underground network of smaller pipelines. As proven reserves of natural gas declined in the 1970s, research was conducted on ways to import natural gas. U.S. firms turned to the proven technology of liquefying gas at low temperatures and pumping it aboard specially designed tankers for shipment to the United States. When the liquefied natural gas (LNG) arrives at its destination, it is regasified and fed into the pipeline system.

Products

Consumer products such as gasoline and home heating oil are usually sent directly from the refinery via pipeline, tanker, barge, or railroad to an installation called a *terminal*. A terminal is a storage and

Figure 8.3. Tugboats push barges in for loading at docks. *(Courtesy of Saber Energy, Inc.)*

loading area close to a large population center. Personnel at a terminal are responsible for certain quality checks before they can sell products. These tests may include a flash-point check (fig. 8.4), to verify that each product vaporizes within the specified proper temperature range, and a gravity check (fig. 8.5). Aviation fuel is sent to a laboratory for testing before it can be sold. These tests have to be repeated at the terminal because products may have changed during transport from the refinery.

From the terminal, products are transported to bulk plants serving smaller communities or directly to service stations, airports, homes, or businesses. Although a large volume of bulk product is transported by rail, barge, and coastal tanker, delivery by road vehicle is the most popular form of final distribution. Larger industrial consumers, the exception, are usually supplied by water, rail, or pipeline.

Figure 8.4. A flash-point indicator is used to verify fuel specifications.

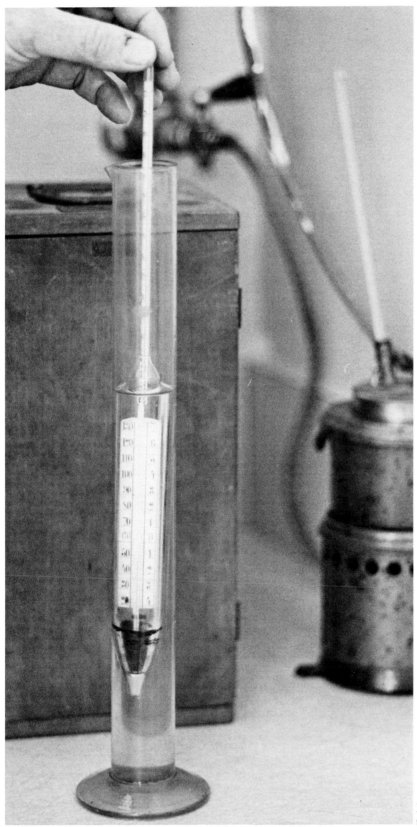

Figure 8.5. Tester checks gravity of the fuel at the terminal.

Figure 8.6. Truck operator prepares to load up with several types of products at the terminal.

Figure 8.7. Truck is loaded by attaching the rack hoses.

Most terminals will have several truck loading devices, commonly called *loading racks* (fig. 8.6–8.9). The rack is equipped to load the truck compartments with several kinds of products at the same time. The rack is also equipped to pipe vapors off the top of the truck compartments in vapor recovery efforts. The terminal, which may belong to a refinery or larger oil company, will often sell to a number of different kinds of consumers. The owning oil company may supply its own branded filling stations in the area.

Figure 8.8. Truck operator uses card for automatic invoicing.

Figure 8.9. Terminal meter records type and amount of products purchased.

Jobbers, independent middlemen in the industry, may contract with the terminal's owning company as an agent to sell that brand of product wholesale in a given trade area. (A jobber may also own a retail outlet where he resells the product from the terminal.) Independent filling station owners may purchase their fuels from the terminal or from jobbers. Jobbers may purchase propane and butane to deliver to rural homes. At a large terminal, the combination of such different types of orders, loading instructions, dispatching, and invoicing creates a great deal of physical supervision and paperwork.

Terminal operation is another area of the oil industry that has become computerized. Using automatic invoicing, data can be transmitted quickly to a company's centralized computer. Such information also facilitates centralized credit control, sales statistics, vehicle statistics, and stock records. A number of physical functions previously performed manually are now automated. During truck loading, the identity of the driver and vehicle, the amount and description of product exchanged, and its destination can be recorded automatically. Some terminals are equipped with visual display units that enable terminal employees to call up certain computerized files at the head office in order to obtain consumer data. The minicomputer is making possible the storage of customer data and the proper invoicing at a terminal itself.

When a truck is loaded, discharge plans must be designed for optimal off-loading performance. Industrial customers and many filling stations can take full truck loads, but in the case of farms and domestic customers, the amount of fuel needed often will not fill up a truck. Thus, a terminal must cater also to the small-drop market. Computers often are used in this area also to plan vehicle loadings and routings. This minimization of distribution time, and thus costs, is of major importance to all marketing companies.

Advertising

Another function of marketing that has evolved over the century is advertising and promotional activities. Traditional methods of the Majors have been newspaper and magazine ads and the sponsorship of radio and television programs. More recently, the Majors have tried to educate the public on the role that the oil industry plays in the national and world economy. This type of advertising functions as institutional advertising. Philanthropic examples such as the Exxon Foundation, sponsoring research and programming in the humanities on television, bring the company's name frequently before the public without actually advertising products.

Other more direct customer appeals have included the giving away of road maps, dishes, and premiums at service stations and the awarding of trading stamps. Some companies offered travel club advantages such as free trip routing, motel credit, bail bond protection, and towing service. The use of gasoline credit cards expanded after World War II, and some companies began to offer extended terms for tire and accessory purchases. Mass mailings of credit applications were made to attract new customers, such as graduating college classes.

After the dramatic increase in the cost of crude that occurred in 1973, American oil companies began to take measures to cut down on expenses. As well as closing down unprofitable stations, companies reduced their giveaways and marginal services at stations. Credit card accounts were no longer widely solicited. The option of self-service was offered to somewhat offset the rising price of gasoline. Another promotional device that customers could no longer count on were the price wars, which had been widely advertised in certain areas to draw customers to the lowest priced stations.

Thus have the functions of marketing ebbed and waned over the century as political pressures have either increased or decreased the power of a free competitive market. As the market has grown more complex and dependent on unpredictable forces, the need for planning has developed into a larger part of the marketing role. Computerization has been utilized at many levels of marketing activities, perhaps demonstrating the greatest change in this century's total effort to market the variety of petroleum products now available.

Conclusion

RETAIL SALES OF PETROLEUM PRODUCTS

Examining how the crude barrel is broken down into its marketable products is important, since most creature comforts result from products and services using some form of petroleum. Besides providing for most transportation modes, petroleum products figure in housing (fuel and electricity), clothing (petroleum-based synthetic fabrics), and food (fertilizers and pesticides). Beyond these basic needs provided for by energy-intensive goods are a host of petroleum-derived products that add to modern man's quality of life. Marketable petroleum products can be divided into broad classes that provide for transportation, electrical generation and industry, home and commerce, agriculture, and petrochemicals These general areas are supplied by different *cuts* of crude (separated by their boiling points from high to low) including gases, liquefied petroleum gas, gasoline, aviation fuels, kerosine, diesel fuel, lubricating oils, waxes, fuel oils, and miscellaneous products. Figure 8.10 shows a comparison of the ways the crude barrel has been divided over the century.

Consumers of automotive fuels experience the effects of petroleum marketing most directly at the retail outlet—the service station (8.11). Several transactions occur in the marketing chain of operations as gasoline moves from the terminal to the station pump. One of the most important to the refiner, distributor, retailer, and consumer is the price structuring.

Transportation

Automotive fuels

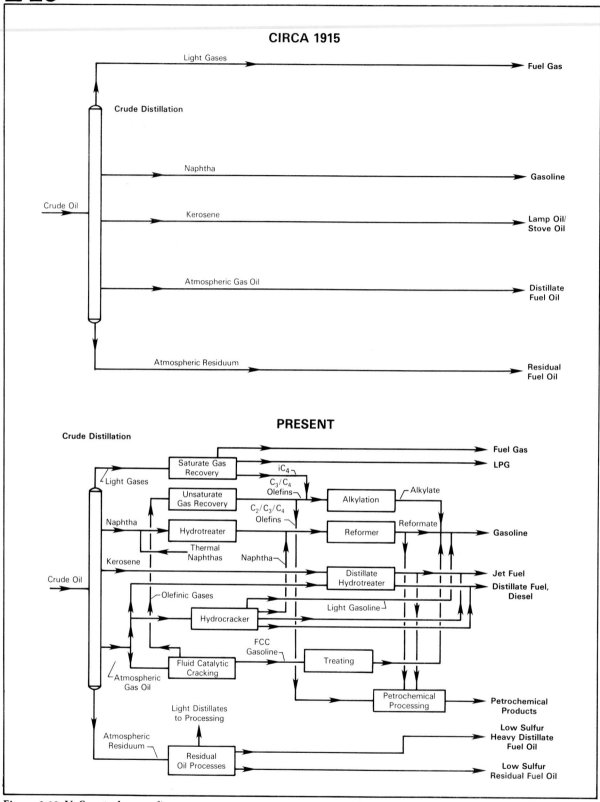

Figure 8.10. U. S. petroleum refinery use of crude.

Figure 8.11. Self-service helps the consumer keep the price of gasoline down.

This particular chain of events begins with the publishing every other week of refinery prices in different geographic areas. These refinery sale prices have been regulated by the Department of Energy (DOE). Each refinery that sells in an area will post its prices for different kinds of products to be sold to different kinds of buyers. For instance, unleaded gas will be sold at a lower price to a jobber than it will be to a retailer, who buys it at the *dealer tankwagon* (DTW) price. Table 8.2 is an excerpt from such a price sheet. When the

Table 8.2
Excerpt of Prices at Key Terminals

Albuquerque, NM	Chevron	Conoco	Exxon	Fina	Husky	K-McGee	Mobil	Phillip	Shamrck	Shell	Vickers		
No. 2 reseller	78.90*	82.35		80.60	82.90		84.65c	82.20	79.75c		79.00		
Reg. gas reseller				91.85	94.90	91.25			89.75d		92.19		
Reg. gas DTW	89.70		96.40				95.80			96.60			
Unl. gas reseller				94.85	97.15	95.25			92.75d		97.19		
Unl. gas DTW	92.70		100.40				99.80			99.60			
Amarillo, TX	Chevron	Conoco	Fina	Foremst	Husky	K-McGee	Phillip	Shamrck	Texaco	Tosco			
No. 2 reseller		80.05	80.60c	82.10	82.00	81.35	81.95	79.25c	82.53c	78.15c			
Reg. gas reseller		90.44	90.95	91.70	94.90	91.25	91.15	88.70d		90.15			
Reg. gas DTW	88.40						95.30		100.35				
Unl. gas reseller		94.20	93.95	95.70	97.15	95.25	95.15	91.70d		93.90			
Unl. gas DTW	91.40						99.30		104.15				
Birmingham, AL	Amoco	Chevron	Citgo	Conoco	Crown	Exxon	Gulf	Hunt	Marathn	Shell	Tosco	Triangl	Union
No. 2 reseller		81.40*	80.99c	82.75	79.00			82.50	80.50		78.35c	79.00c	82.10
Reg. gas reseller	93.65d		90.20	89.55	90.25			92.75	90.00		88.90	90.26	92.85
Reg. gas DTW	96.90	89.50				95.40	95.00			96.10			96.30
Unl. gas reseller	97.40d		95.70	93.55	94.25			98.00	94.00		92.65	94.26	94.85
Unl. gas DTW	100.90	92.50				99.40	102.00			99.10			98.30

SOURCE: *Supplement to U.S. Oil Week*, October 6, 1980.

Figure 8.12. Gasoline is unloaded from transport truck for underground storage at service station.

jobber buys the gasoline for resale, he will have to perhaps store and transport it at his own expense (fig. 8.12). Therefore, he is allowed to buy the product at a cheaper refinery price and to tack 8.2 cents (in 1980) onto the refinery invoice price per gallon. When the final retailer buys the gasoline, either from the refinery terminal or from a jobber, he can add on up to 16.8 cents on the gallon for his margin. Either the jobber or the dealer can lower the amount he adds for competitive purposes, but DOE will not allow him at any one time to go above a certain maximum lawful ceiling price.

For purposes of example, assume that one of the refineries offered unleaded gas reseller at $1.00 per gallon. When the jobber picked up a load of this gasoline at a Texas refinery terminal, he would pay the $1.00, plus 4 cents federal tax, plus 5 cents state tax for each gallon of the product he bought. He would add to this *invoice purchase price* of $1.09 perhaps 1 cent for freight charges to take the product to his bulk plant, and thus arrive at his actual *acquisition price* of $1.10 per gallon. To this sum, he could add his allowable margin of 8.2 cents and establish a dealer tankwagon cost of $1.18 and 0.2 cents per gallon. When the final retail dealer buys the product at this DTW price, he is allowed to add 16.8 cents, which would make the final price to the consumer $1.35 per gallon.

To the consumer, the most important characteristic of purchased gasoline is probably its antiknock value or *octane number*. This number represents a measure of the gasoline's efficiency of combustion, a property that can be tested under laboratory conditions. Gasolines are marketed according to their research octane numbers. A level of about 100 is considered a good antiknock value for premium gasolines in most countries. A straight-run fraction of crude from 30°C to about 200°C (the gasoline range) would produce violently heavy knock. Therefore, gasoline blends use processed concentrates of those hydrocarbons that have high octane numbers. These include aromatics (obtained from catalytic reforming), olefins (obtained from catalytic cracking or polymerization), and isoparaffins (obtained from isomerization or alkylation). Since the government has required that new cars be manufactured to use only unleaded fuel, oil companies have produced a *super* unleaded gasoline with an octane rating of around 90 (fig. 8.13).

Figure 8.13. Super unleaded gasoline is now offered by some service stations.

Aviation fuels

The need for air-transport fuels has developed dramatically in this century, as the size, capacity, and number of worldwide airliners have all increased. The demands placed on fuel quality for aircraft are, of course, more stringent than those for automotive fuel. Aviation fuel must be free of contaminants (water or dirt), be pumpable at low temperatures, meet regulations for specific gravity and caloric value, and burn cleanly and remain stable when heated to high temperatures.

Aviation fuel falls into the two categories of piston-engine fuel and fuel for combustion in gas turbines (or jet engines). Most passenger-carrying and military aircraft have changed over from piston engines to gas turbines. However, a need still exists for high-octane aviation fuels for piston engines in older aircraft and smaller recreation and business planes (fig. 8.14). Marketing planners have had to try to predict the rate of changeover each year from aviation piston-engine fuel to jet fuel. The most commonly used fuels for jet aircraft are JP 4 and JP 5. JP 5 is kerosine supplied from crude as a straight-run fraction in the range of 150° C to 250° C. A blend of straight-run fractions covering the range on crude from about 30° C to 260° C is made to supply the aviation fuel called JP 4.

As the quality of aviation fuel has increased, so also has the design of equipment for its storage and transfer from the refinery to the airplane. Because its contamination could cause fatal accidents in the air, aviation fuel movement is monitored very carefully. Laboratory tests are repeated at different stages to guarantee product specifications. Usually, a jobber will buy from a terminal and then store the fuel close to an airport. The different kinds of fuel are color

Figure 8.14. Small aircraft, such as this piston-engine plane, uses aviation gasoline for its fuel.

coded for sight identification when loading and servicing. Refueling rate has improved greatly to meet scheduled aircraft turnaround time. Large refueling trucks carry the fuel out to an airplane where it is pumped under controlled pressure into the aircraft's tanks (fig. 8.15). Hydrant systems are also used when underground pipe work carries the fuel from storage tanks to aircraft parking areas.

Marine fuels

Oil firing, rather than coal burning, became popular for steamships during the first half of the century. Oil allowed greater steaming distance, was safer and easier to stoke, and took up less storage space. The refueling of ships became simpler, and oil burned cleaner. With the development of the marine diesel engine, more new ships were built equipped with oil engines.

Marine fuels consist of both fuel oil and diesel fuel. Since ships run at a lower rotational speed than automotive diesel engines, marine diesel engines will accept deeper cuts into crude oil. A marine diesel oil often consists of a blend of gas oil and some residual material. Gas oil is generally defined as being somewhere in the boiling range of 200° C to 350° C. Because of rising prices, ship owners have recently tended to operate diesel engines on high-viscosity residual fuels.

The actual refueling of ships with oil is referred to as *bunkering*. Bunkering may be achieved through pipelines, from barges, or by road or railcar tanks. When, because of size, a ship cannot come alongside a wharf, submarine or floating lines or refueling barges can be used to refuel the ship's tank (bunker) while it is moored at sea.

Figure 8.15. A turbine-engine commercial airliner is filled with jet fuel.

Electrical generation and industry

The industrial sector consumes more than half of the total output of the world's petroleum products. A large portion, especially natural gas, goes into the creation of electricity at generating plants (fig. 8.16). Oil (fig. 8.17) and coal are also fuel sources for generating plants. The gas, oil, or coal is burned to heat water that provides steam to turn turbines. The energy created by the turbines is converted by generators into electricity.

Figure 8.16. Natural gas enters this electricity generating plant through pipelines.

Figure 8.17. Oil is stored in tanks for alternate use as fuel for generating electricity.

Coal-fired plants must have higher stacks, from 450 to 600 feet, in order to release the hot gases high in the atmosphere (figs. 8.18 and 8.19). Stack emissions are carefully monitored both at the site and at various distances within the prevailing windstream.

Another large portion of petroleum products goes to manufacturers who require energy to run their machines and processes. An example is the steel industry, where thousands of tons of fuel oil are consumed annually to run the plants. As well as fuel oil and natural gas, petroleum supplies industry with a wide range of lubricants and process oils.

Products for industry may be marketed directly in bulk to large consumers like the armed forces, railways, and major manufacturers, or indirectly through jobbers to smaller consumers. Sales transactions tend to be lengthy and complex.

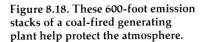

Figure 8.18. These 600-foot emission stacks of a coal-fired generating plant help protect the atmosphere.

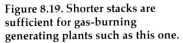

Figure 8.19. Shorter stacks are sufficient for gas-burning generating plants such as this one.

Figure 8.20. A myriad of household appliances are operated by gas and electricity.

Home and commerce

The conversion from solid fuel to oil for heating the home has been widespread in this century. And, since the 1973 rise in crude prices, the use of gas and electricity has intensified. Both natural gas and electricity provide the convenient aspect of being piped and wired into the consumer's property, while oil has to be delivered by truck. Natural gas has become the major competitor to oil for heating; electricity, being a secondary energy source, is usually a more expensive alternative for heating, but it is used extensively for cooling and for operating household appliances, tools, instruments, and the like (fig. 8.20). In addition to natural gas, liquefied petroleum gas (LPG)—specifically propane and butane—is used for heating in rural areas and other locations not serviced by natural gas (fig. 8.21). LPG tanks are usually purchased and maintained by the property owners and filled by local distributors.

Both natural gas and electricity come under the heading of public utilities. Because gas pipes and electrical wires must be part of a community network, the community contracts as a whole for services. Thus, the utility is considered a "public" service, and the two sources of energy are subject to state regulations, which influence their pricing to consumers.

Figure 8.21. A butane tank furnishes heating fuel for this farm home.

Figure 8.22. A portable propane tank furnishes fuel for the farmer's tractor and other farm implements.

Although gas and electricity are used increasingly for residences, heating oil continues to be marketed to heat commercial buildings such as hospitals, schools, and factories. Fuel oils for domestic burners are distilled from the deeper cuts of crude after the lighter products have been taken off. Domestic fuel oils are divided into two grades for marketing—*number one oil* and *number two oil*—as specified by the American Society for Testing and Materials. Marketing and distribution are conducted in a manner similar to that of gasoline, with the jobber's role being crucial for deliveries and sales to individual customers.

Agriculture

Petroleum products play a vital role in farming today. Using the internal-combustion engine to power the tractor was greatly responsible for transforming the traditional rural farm into a modern industry. The development of diesel fuels and LPG for tractors and other mechanized implements, as well as the development of proper lubricants for those machines, has revolutionized farming (fig. 8.22).

Other vital petroleum derivatives used for agriculture are the chemicals used for fertilizer. A range of petroleum-based chemicals are also used to protect crops from plant and animal pests. Methods of marketing this wide array of agricultural products vary. Sometimes marketing companies sell directly to the farmers, sometimes agents or jobbers are used, and sometimes a farmer buys from a local distributor (fig. 8.23).

Figure 8.23. Fertilizer is poured into the hopper of a spreader for use on a rancher's grazing land.

Marketing petrochemicals is different in several respects from marketing conventional petroleum products. Few petrochemicals are end products themselves. They are usually primary feedstocks or intermediate chemicals that are sold to manufacturers. Factory processes then turn them into such articles as tires, fabrics, plastics, and a host of other products. Also, some primary petrochemicals are made as intermediates for the manufacture of other petrochemicals.

Volumes of petrochemicals are relatively small compared to gasolines and fuel oils. And most sales of petrochemicals are by long-term contracts, with little spot selling to influence price fluctuation. Therefore, plant output is easier to predict even before the plant is built. On the other hand, market development is more of a challenge in petrochemicals than in conventional petroleum products. As more and more imaginative end products are developed from petrochemicals, the public must be educated as to their modern usefulness. Television advertising has been very useful in showing the innovation, for instance, of such a product as Saran wrap. Petrochemical products can also die an untimely death for their parent companies, as an even more useful chemical may be invented out of petroleum feedstocks. For this reason, vertically integrated oil companies have often stayed out of petrochemical marketing. They may instead sell their feedstocks or primary petrochemicals directly to chemical companies or manufacturers.

Thus, a variety of petroleum products are available from various cuts of crude (fig. 8.24).

Federal price regulations

The end pricing of petroleum products is obviously affected by governmental regulations controlling the wellhead prices of crude oil and natural gas. Among the forces that create prices—availability of reserves, entrepreneurial freedom, and market competition—governmental regulation is a prime contributing factor. The oil industry has long operated under governmental regulation, tax incentives, and research and development assistance. The prevailing emphasis since the enactment of President Jimmy Carter's National Energy Plan (NEP) and the Natural Gas Policy Act (NGPA) is towards deregulation. Wellhead prices will be allowed to rise to world levels to encourage further exploration and development, but increased profits will be returned to the public in the form of the "windfall profits" tax.

An elaborate set of rules enables the phasing out by 1985 of many natural gas price controls at the wellhead. Traditionally, *intrastate gas* (gas that does not cross state lines as it is piped from production to consumer) has not been federally controlled. *Interstate gas* (gas which does travel across state lines) has been federally regulated. The

CHECK LIST OF COMMERCIAL PETROLEUM PRODUCTS

THEIR SOURCE AND END USES

From *Petroleum Products Handbook* by Virgil B. Guthrie. Copyright © 1960 by the McGraw-Hill Book Company, Inc. Used with the permission of McGraw-Hill Book Company.

From Natural Gas

LP-GAS
Dom. and ind. fuels, motor fuel, gas enrichment, solvent, treating and varied ind. uses

PROPANE
Component of LP-Gas, raw material for petrochemicals

BUTANE
Component of LP-Gas and of motor and aviation gasoline, raw material for petrochemicals

AMMONIA
(by syn. from methane)
Fertilizer, petrochemical mfg.

CARBON BLACK
Rubber reinforcing agent, ink mfg., carbon paper, battery cells

LAMP BLACK
Tinting paints and lacquers

ETHANE AND OTHER RAW MATERIALS FOR PETRO-CHEMICAL MFG.

SULFUR
(from hydrogen sulfide)

NATURAL GASOLINE
Component of motor and aviation gasoline, special solvents, refinery processing material

From Refinery Gases

Noncondensable Gases

HYDROGEN
(from cat. reforming)
Chemical and ind. processing

AMMONIA
(from hydrogen)

CARBON BLACK

SULFUR
(from hydrogen sulfide)

Liquefied Gases

REFINERY LP-GAS

MOTOR FUELS

Processed Derivatives Olefins, Diolefins

BUTADIENE
Syn. rubber, petrochemical and plastics mfg.

ETHYLENE
Polyethylene mfg., raw materials for petrochem. mfg. and alcohols

POLYMERS
Lube oil additives

ANTIKNOCK AGENTS
Aviation gasoline blending

ALCOHOLS, ESTERS KETONES, RESINS
Antifreeze agents, drug and lacquer solvents

SYN. PLASTIC WAXES
Inks and paints

From Light Distillates from Refining Petroleum

Light Naphthas

GAS-MACHINE GASOLINE

SPECIAL GASOLINES

Intermediate Naphthas

AVIATION GASOLINE

MOTOR GASOLINE

MARINE GASOLINE

COMMERCIAL SOLVENTS
Rubber, lacquer and pesticide diluents

BENZENE
High-octane gasoline component, solvents, petrochemical mfg.

TOLUENE
Solvent, high-octane blending agent, chemical intermediate, explosives

XYLENE
High-octane gasoline blending agent, lacquer and enamels mfg., chemicals intermediate

Heavy Naphthas

VM&P NAPHTHA
Thinner for paints, varnishes, lacquers, type cleaner, mfg. cements and adhesives

STODDARD SOLVENT
Special solvent for dry-cleaning trade

MINERAL SPIRITS
Thinner for paints and varnishes, turpentine substitute

Jet Fuel Component

The term "jet fuel" includes fuels for aircraft gas turbine engines of both the jet thrust and propeller type

Figure 8.24. Commercial petroleum products, their sources, and their end uses (*Courtesy of McGraw-Hill Book Company*)

From Middle Distillates from Refining Petroleum

KEROSINE
Illuminating oil, range oil, stove fuel, tractor fuel, pesticide, diluent
|
JET FUEL

Gas Oil
|
DIESEL FUELS
|
DISTILLATE HEATING OILS
|
WATER GAS CARBURETION OILS
|
METALLURGICAL FUELS
|
NAPHTHENIC ACIDS
Detergents, paint dryers, lubricating oil additives, pesticides

ABSORBER OILS
Used in the recovery of natural gasoline, gasoline, aromatics, and other light hydrocarbon compounds by absorption methods

From Distillate Lubricating Oil Stocks

White Oils (technical)
|
INSECTICIDE AND SPRAY OIL DILUENT
|
BAKERS, FRUIT PACKERS, CANDY MAKERS, EGG PACKERS, SLAB OILS
|
HYDRAULIC OILS
|
RECOIL OILS
|
White Oils (medicinal)
|
INTERNAL LUBRICANTS
|
SALVES, GREASES, OINTMENTS, COSMETICS

Saturating Oils, Emulsifying, Flotation Oils
|
PAPER, LEATHER, WOOL, TWINE OILS
|
COAL SPRAY OILS
|
DUST-LAYING OILS
|
TEXTILE OILS
|
METAL RECOVERY, QUENCHING OILS

PETROLEUM WAX (PARAFFIN AND MICROCRYSTALLINE)
Paper manufacturing, sanitary containers, waxed wrappers, candle making, match making, drugs, cosmetics, canning, sealing wax, insulation and coatings, candy, chewing-gum manufacture
|
FATTY ACIDS
Lubricating oil pour point depressors, grease and soap lubricant
|
FATTY ALCOHOLS AND SULPHATES
Rubber compounds, detergents, wetting agents

Light Lube Oils
|
TURBINE OILS
|
LIGHT SPINDLE OILS
|
TRANSFORMER OILS
|
HOUSEHOLD LUBRICANTS
|
COMPRESSOR OILS
|
ICE MACHINE OILS
|
METER, DUST-LAYING, TEMPERING OILS

Medium Lube Oils
|
MOTOR OILS
|
AIRCRAFT OILS
|
DIESEL OILS
|
JOURNAL OILS
|
ENGINE OILS
|
RAILROAD OILS
|
CUTTING, METAL WORKING OIL BASE

Heavy Lube Oils
|
LUBRICATING GREASES
|
STEAM CYL. OILS
|
VALVE OILS
|
TRANSMISSION OILS
|
PRINTING OILS
|
BLACK OILS
|
TEMPERING OILS

From Lubricating Oil Stocks Bottoms

MEDICINAL PETROLATUMS
Salves, creams, ointments, petroleum jelly

TECHNICAL PETROLATUMS
Rust-preventing compounds, rubber softeners, wire rope lubricants, cable coating compounds

From Residues from Petroleum Distillation

Residual Fuel Oils
|
HEATING OILS
|
BOILER FUEL
|
BUNKER C FUEL
|
WOOD PRESERVATIVE
|
GAS-MANUFACTURE OILS

Asphalt
ASPHALT CEMENT
Paving, surfacing, construction materials, base for paints, lacquers, inks, roofing compounds, undercoatings
|
LIQUID ASPHALT
Cut-back asphalts, road oils, emulsion bases, saturants, roofing compounds
|
BLOWN ASPHALT
Waterproofings, rubber substitutes, insulating asphalts, roof coatings

Petroleum Coke
RAW COKE
Ind. and dom. fuel, calcium carbide manufacture, foundry and blast furnace coke
|
CALCINED COKE
Aluminum anodes, furnace electrodes and linings, graphite specialties

Refinery Sludges
|
SULFONIC ACID
Saponification agents, emulsifiers, demulsifying agents, special oils

Figure 8.24, continued

NGPA has sought to equalize gas prices in producing and consuming areas by involving intrastate gas in its phasing out of controls. Gas is priced according to a six-tier system of definitions:

(1) new gas;

(2) old, interstate gas that is subject to existing contracts;

(3) old, interstate gas that will be made available at the expiration of existing interstate contracts;

(4) the same class of gas formerly sold in intrastate commerce;

(5) specific categories of high cost gas; and

(6) synthetic natural gas.[6]

As the resulting change in pricing occurs, several marketing problems will arise. Should gas sell at prices based on the actual cost of production? Should different classes of users—industrial and residential—be offered different prices resulting from the different tiers? If gas prices are allowed to rise to compete as a Btu equivalent of world market crude, will that action allow OPEC and the oil industry to set the price of U.S. natural gas as well as oil?

Crude-oil prices at the wellhead are affected similarly in an effort to decontrol by September 30, 1981. Four tiers will divide pricing among—

(1) old oil;

(2) previously discovered oil;

(3) the current world price for newly discovered oil (that is, oil from a well that is either 2.5 miles from an existing onshore well as of April 20, 1977, or more than 1,000 feet deeper than any existing well within a 2.5-mile radius of such a well); and

(4) incremental tertiary recovery and stripper oil production that is free of controls.[7]

Again, many considerations arise out of the challenge of deregulation and the enactment of the involved phasing-out entanglements. How much will the resulting increased retail product prices encourage consumers to conserve? Will the end prices slow down the economy and unduly affect the poor who are dependent on energy-intensive goods? Will the increased profits to producers encourage further exploration and development enough to offset the disadvantages of higher prices? And, finally, will the administrative and legal costs to the government of enacting such systems unduly burden the economy until deregulation occurs?

All of these possibilities must be considered by a petroleum marketing planner. They are the challenges presented daily also to middlemen involved in sales and finally to the end consumer—the American public.

---

6. Dudley J. Burton, *The Governance of Energy: Problems, Prospects, and Underlying Issues* (New York: Praeger Publishers, 1980), p. 77.

7. Burton, p. 78.

General Overview
of the Industry

Outer Continental Shelf (OCS) oil and natural gas will become increasingly important to the U.S. energy picture. At present, OCS oil has contributed only 5 percent of domestic production, but it comprises over 20 percent of national reserves.[1] As onshore oil and gas reserves are depleted, dependence on offshore production will require technologically advanced methods of recovery and transportation in order to take the fullest advantage of those resources. Only major firms can afford to drill for OCS oil because of the enormous expenditures involved; costs have been rapidly rising because of increasing leasing costs and capital costs.

1. Hossein G. Askari and Timothy W. Ruefli, "The National Energy Plan and the Leasing of Federal Energy Lands," in *National Energy Policy: A Continuing Assessment* (Austin: Council on Energy Resources, The University of Texas at Austin, 1978).

EFFECTS OF LEASING FEDERAL LANDS

Economic experts have leveled several criticisms at the Bureau of Land Management's handling of the leasing of federal lands. The federal government has to consider the overall state of the nation, including the environment, and that concern is reflected in the BLM's allocation of federal lands for leasing. Some experts in the field complain that while 15 percent of developed oil reserves, 15 percent of discovered oil resources, and perhaps 33 percent of undiscovered oil resources are on federal lands, no more than 4 percent of the federal offshore holdings have ever been developed for oil and gas (fig. 9.1). They further claim that 75 percent of the onshore federal estate are withdrawn or seriously restricted from energy and mineral development.[2]

Statistics published in the *Congressional Journal* (September, 1975) show that of the 1.5 billion acres of land in the United States available for mining, two-thirds of it has been withdrawn from mineral development. These figures are accounted for by lands withdrawn for national parks, military and civic purposes, military reservations, Indian reservations, and wilderness areas. Even though the figures do not necessarily reflect the impact of the withdrawals on mining in general or on development of a specific mineral in particular, the withdrawals, which can be enacted by bureaus in the Department of Interior without congressional hearings, do add to the general uncertainty of leasing.

Other uncertainties concerning federal energy reserves may be laid at the feet of the federal government: in particular, the U.S. Department of the Interior "currently does not know exactly how much federal land there is, or exactly where it is located."[3] This information is being catalogued, but even when it is available, federal lands are often discontinuous, being broken up by areas of private ownership. This situation results in lease areas that are too small for commercial production. A related problem is that the productivity and value of any particular reserve often depend on how high prices for petroleum are at the time. If prices are high, deposits that are otherwise economically unfeasible become recoverable. Given the ever-increasing demand for fuel, many deposits that were once considered too expensive to produce are being reclassified.

2. W. W. Rostow, William L. Fisher, and George Kozmetsky, "The National Energy Plan: An Overview," in *Preliminary Assessment of the President's National Energy Plan* (Austin: The University of Texas at Austin, 1977), pp. 28–29.
3. Askari and Ruefli, pp. 317–318.

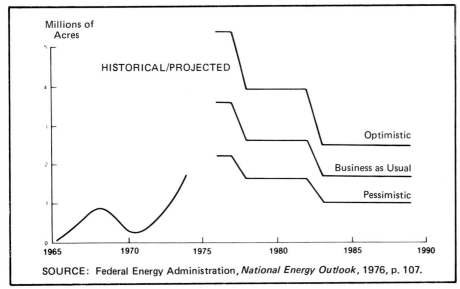

Figure 9.1. Outer Continental Shelf leasing schedules

THE SITUATION AT HOME AND ABROAD

Since the early 1970s, the energy crisis has become an important factor in the internal and international politics of the United States. Deregulation of natural gas has been one of the most important issues facing the Congress and the President for years; the question of expanded oil imports is not only a matter of concern to the petroleum industry, the consumer, and the U.S. government, but also a matter of international concern (fig. 9.2). The leading world economic powers have consistently put pressure on the United States to lower its petroleum imports because the United States' balance-of-payments situation and, therefore, the dollar are both declining against the major currencies of the world. Foreign powers attribute the dollar's fall to the United States' continuing importation of over half of the world's petroleum demand yearly. Industry spokesmen present the problem as less one of importation than one of artificially low prices: if the consumer were to pay what his gas and oil really cost, then he would cut back voluntarily. And yet the Congress, whose job it is to enact legislation that will encourage energy conservation and protect the economy from spiraling inflation while protecting the dollar abroad and the consumer and industries at home, is under pressure from all sides and finds it very hard to frame adequate legislation. One of the main difficulties is that the reports on supply versus demand vary widely depending on the source of the information.

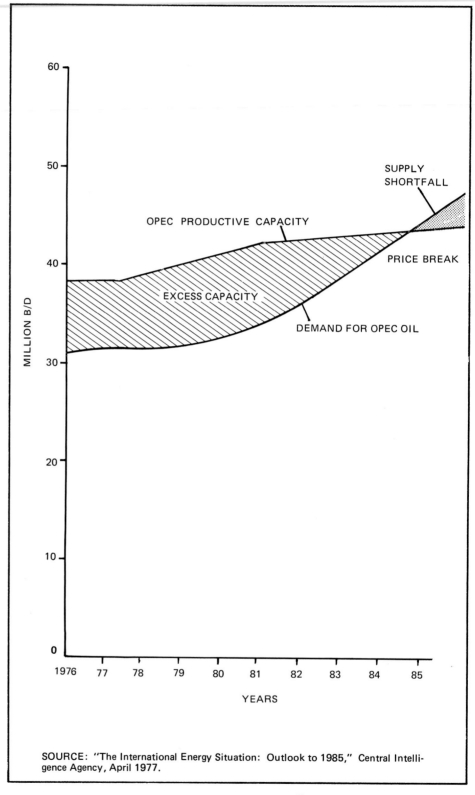

Figure 9.2. Projection of demand and capacity in OPEC production

THE NATURAL GAS SITUATION

The prognosis for the natural gas supply varies greatly, depending on whose figures are cited, but the overall picture for the United States is that undiscovered resources, proved reserves, and total indicated remaining resources of natural gas fall short of the growing demand for the clean energy that natural gas provides. According to the Interstate Natural Gas Association of America (INGAA), a thirty-five- to sixty-year supply of gas from conventional sources is estimated to be recoverable from onshore and offshore regions. And as of 1974, the American Gas Association (AGA) charted reserves at 205.4 trillion cubic feet (Tcf) (fig. 9.3). While accepting the AGA reserve figure, the *National Energy Outlook,* published by the Federal Energy Administration (FEA), quotes statistics that show the United States is using approximately 22 Tcf of gas per year, which sounds as though it would deplete a 205-Tcf reserve in less than ten years.

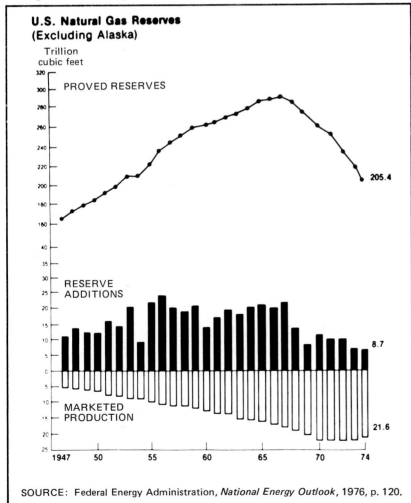

SOURCE: Federal Energy Administration, *National Energy Outlook*, 1976, p. 120.

Figure 9.3. U.S. natural gas reserves, excluding Alaska

But the contradiction is only an apparent one, which points up the real problem in figuring out what is the natural gas or oil situation. There are so many different estimates and terms for talking about reserves that even the most careful analyst or legislator can easily become confused. For example, tables 9.1 and 9.2 and figures 9.3 and 9.4 present varying estimates of natural gas reserves.

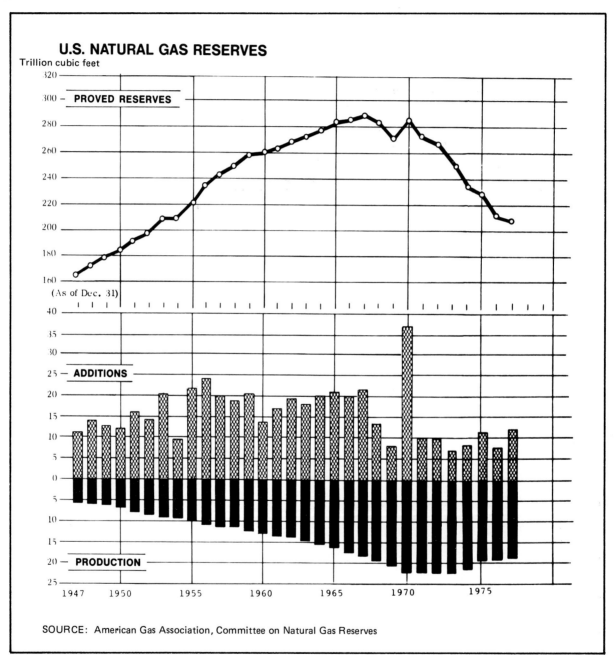

Figure 9.4. U.S. natural gas reserves
*(Courtesy of American Gas Association
Committee on Natural Gas Reserves)*

Table 9.1
Estimated Potential Supply of Natural Gas
by Depth Increments as of December 31, 1976
(trillion cubic feet)

	Probable	Possible	Speculative
Onshore (drilling depth)			
Less than 15,000 feet	106	156	99
15,000 to 30,000 feet	35	79	26 to 76
Total onshore	141	235	125 to 175
Offshore (water depth)			
Less than 600 feet	51	60	60
600 to 1,500 feet	—	23	3
Total offshore	51	83	63
Total lower 48 states	192	318	188 to 238
Alaska	23	45	157
Total United States	215	363	345 to 395

SOURCE: *Potential Supply of Natural Gas as of December 31, 1976*, Report of the Potential Gas Committee.

Table 9.2
Estimated Gas Resources and Reserves
(trillion cubic feet)

Source of Estimate	Year of Estimate	Potential Resources[a]			1976 Proved Reserves	Total Remaining Resources[b]
		New Fields	Old Fields	Total		
U.S. Geological Survey	1974	322–655	202	524–857	216	722–1,055
National Academy of Sciences	1974	530	118	648	216	846
Exxon Base	1974	342–942	56–321	423–1,143	216	621–1,341
Potential Gas Committee	1976	708–758	216	923–973	216	1,139–1,189

[a] Does not include possible resources from unconventional sources such as coal-bed degasification, Devonian shale, Rocky Mountain tight-gas formation, geopressured resources, and biomass and coal gasification.

[b] As of December 31, 1976. Estimates are corrected for gas consumed since the date of resource estimate.

SOURCE: American Gas Association.

Curtailment

The increase in demand for natural gas has exceeded the supply since the 1970s.[4] The growth in U.S. natural gas consumption from 1920 to 1974 meant that the industry that once supplied 4 percent of the nation's fuel had taken over 30 percent of the market by 1974 (fig. 9.5).[5] The result of excess demand has been significant curtailment—generally defined as contractual requirements less deliveries—by approximately thirty of the forty-eight major pipeline firms. However, six of these accounted for approximately 65 percent of the projected firm curtailments and about 40 percent of the total firm requirements (fig. 9.6).

New sources of gas

Alternatives to conventional sources of natural gas that are being developed are importation of liquefied natural gas (LNG), Mexican gas, and Alaskan gas; coal gasification; and the development of techniques by which geopressured resources can be tapped. In addition, the industry also points out that more natural gas from conventional sources will be available immediately following price deregulation, because resources that were unprofitable to produce under regulation will be developed when the companies can afford to do so.

4. Federal Energy Administration, *National Energy Outlook*, 1976, p. 112.
5. *National Energy Outlook.*

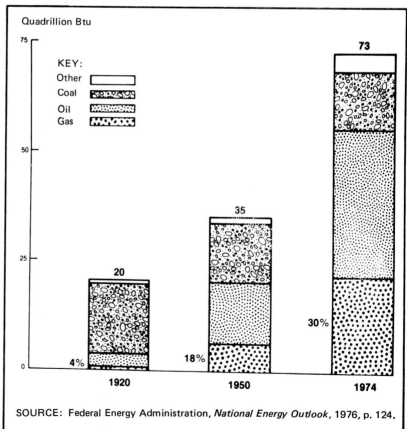

Figure 9.5. Growth in U.S. natural gas consumption, 1920–1974

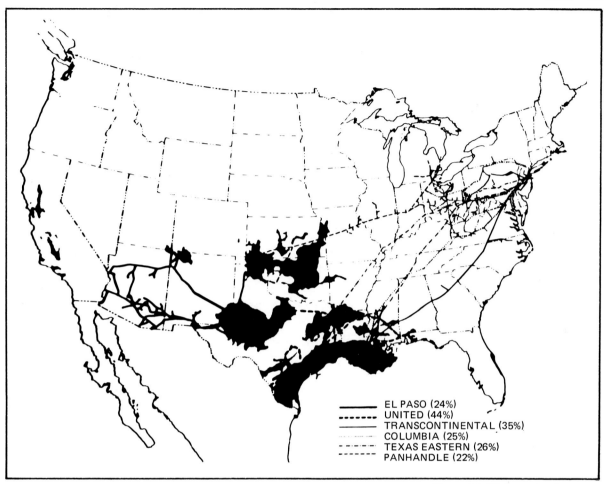

EL PASO (24%)
UNITED (44%)
TRANSCONTINENTAL (35%)
COLUMBIA (25%)
TEXAS EASTERN (26%)
PANHANDLE (22%)

Figure 9.6. Major natural gas producing regions and pipelines with significant curtailments

The federal government is considering deregulation of natural gas as a part of the energy package, but they are expected to maintain stringent controls over the leasing of federal lands and Outer Continental Shelf lands as a way of allocating the resources of the country and controlling the rate of resource depletion. The government is less willing than industry to build up further patterns of dependence on foreign exporters of petroleum products; therefore, the worldwide petroleum resources that figure largely in some industry statistics are not included in some government statistics. Dependence, vulnerability to foreign political manipulations, and potential trouble caused by sudden interruption or abrupt increase in price are three of the significant major issues associated with supplemental petroleum imports to the United States.

Liquefied natural gas

LNG is natural gas of 1,000 Btu/cf or higher—that is, of pipeline quality—that is converted to a liquid by lowering the temperature to approximately −260°F. (Btu stands for British thermal unit and is a measure of the heat content of a fuel. One Btu is the quantity of heat required to raise the temperature of 1 pound of water 1 degree Fahrenheit when the temperature of the water is at or near 39.2°F.) This process reduces the volume by 623:1, and approximately 15 percent of the energy is consumed by the transformation.[6] Large-scale transportation of LNG is one of the newest developments by which the petroleum industry and pipeline companies have attempted to keep vital supplies of natural gas available to consumers (fig. 9.7). In 1969 one company began a project designed to supply 1 billion cubic feet of gas a day from Algeria to the East Coast.[7] Nine LNG tankers, each one the size of the Queen Elizabeth II, were to transport the fuel (fig. 9.8); each ship holds 750,000 barrels of LNG, or the equivalent of about 2.5 billion cubic feet of natural gas—enough to supply 16,000 homes for a year.[8] A second project, called Algeria II, will consist of twelve ships with a slightly larger capacity, a terminal located on the Texas Gulf Coast, and a projected first shipment in April 1983.[9]

Synthetic gas from coal

Synthetic gas from coal has been investigated in several pilot projects across the United States, but the commercial viability of a high-Btu synthetic gas has not yet been demonstrated. A low-Btu gas plant has also been considered, but the costs of construction and transportation eliminate this possibility for the immediate future unless cost incentives promote the development of this alternative energy source.

Substitute natural gas

Substitute natural gas (SNG) can be made from liquid petroleum feedstock such as naphtha, crude oil, propane, and butane. Facilities exist for this process, but the plants are used only during peak demand periods and operate at full design capacity for approximately 150 days a year. Thirteen plants are currently in operation; another eight are under construction. The cost of SNG is extremely high in comparison to interstate natural gas at its present regulated price. However, if SNG prices were allowed to be "rolled in" with cheaper domestically produced natural gas, industry feels there would be a price incentive to run the plants at full capacity throughout the year.

6. *National Energy Outlook.*

7. Frank Mangan, *The Pipeliners* (El Paso: Guynes Press, 1977), p. 35.

8. *Natural Gas from Overseas,* Columbia Gas System, April 1978.

9. Juino Dell'Osso, Jr., "Algeria II LNG Project Plans Detailed," *Oil and Gas Journal,* May 29, 1978, p. 65.

Figure 9.7. LNG plants in Iraq, 1977
(Courtesy of Fluor Engineer and Contractor, Inc., and American Petroleum Institute)

Figure 9.8. An LNG tanker undergoes sea trials in the English Channel. *(Courtesy of El Paso Company)*

Tight-formation gas

Gas from tight formations is gas extracted from formations with low permeability, usually the thick, massive sand and shale deposits of the Rocky Mountain states (fig. 9.9). At present the technology for heavy fracturing of the formation necessary to produce the gas is not yet developed. One method is to fracture the zone by nuclear explosives, but this technique has not proved very effective, nor has it proved popular with the citizens of the area, who fear environmental and safety hazards. The other method is massive hydraulic fracturing, but the technology for profitable exploitation of tight-formation natural gas in this area has not been perfected. However, if either stimulation process can be made effective and safe, cumulative recovery of natural gas in place could reach 40 to 50 percent.

Gas from Devonian shale

Gas from Devonian shale formations is potentially another source of natural gas that could be extracted from the approximately 250,000 square miles of formations that underlie the middle and eastern portions of the United States. Massive fracturing, advanced recovery techniques, and a higher return on investment will have to occur before this source of natural gas is available on other than an experimental basis.

Figure 9.9. Seismic operations in the Utah canyon lands, 1977 *(Courtesy of Standard Oil Company and American Petroleum Institute)*

The amount of natural gas that will be available to consumers appears to be largely dependent on governmental energy policies. The government has the responsibility of conserving the natural resources of the nation by reasonable and well-planned leasing of federal lands while it also has the ability to encourage or discourage private enterprise's development of the private sector by governmental pricing regulations. Business has a right to demand a fair return on its investment; if the price is not right, money will not be spent on advancing the research that will eventually result in enhanced-recovery techniques for oil and gas. However, the federal government cannot willingly allow the nation to become more dependent on foreign gas and oil—and thereby leave the country vulnerable to price manipulations and political upheavals of foreign nations—if there are feasible methods of controlling energy usage and thus controlling imports.

THE OIL SITUATION

Once again, the prognosis for oil supplies varies greatly depending on whose figures are cited, but the overall picture for the United States is that estimated undiscovered resources, proved reserves, and total remaining resources of oil fall short of demand. According to the Department of Energy, Energy Data Report for January 31, 1978, the final statistics on supply and demand for oil in 1975 and 1976 show that production of domestic crude, lease condensates, and natural gas plant liquids are declining yearly, while demand for refined products is increasing. The increasing gap in the nation's ability to meet its own demands for oil are met by increasing dependence on foreign imports.

Reserves and resources

The same problem that existed in attempting to compare gas statistics from one source with those from others is also true of facts and figures about oil. Figures that deal with the same general information can be interpreted one way or another, depending on politics or economic bias and the context of discussion. For instance, in the following discussion of the oil situation in the United States, major differences appear in interpretations by the American Petroleum Institute (API), the Federal Energy Administration (FEA), and the Council of Energy Resources (CER).

On one side, the government statistics from FEA's *National Energy Outlook* take into account substantial changes in forecasts, based on its belief that the Tax Reduction Act of 1975 modified the tax and depletion situation, that resource estimates were revised downward by FEA and the U.S. Geological Survey, that the schedule for leasing of Outer Continental Shelf lands was revised upward, that the rate of development for Northern Alaska was revised upward, and so on. Some of the FEA figures are based on a business-as-usual (BAU) supply outlook, which the FEA says represents the USGS geological assessment. In terms of assumptions, the BAU outlook is moderately optimistic in several areas. It assumes that (1) OCS leasing proceeds according to the Department of Interior's announced leasing schedule; (2) tertiary oil-recovery methods prove successful technically and economically and are applied to a moderately optimistic page; (3) oil and gas deregulation occurs over the next few years; and (4) the present provisions of the federal tax code that affect crude-oil economics remain unchanged.

On the other hand, the Council on Energy Resources of The University of Texas at Austin in its discussion of the National Energy Policy[10] refrains from including reserve and resource data from North Alaska and undeveloped offshore areas in projections for production of oil and liquids. Not including discoveries of new fields and reservoirs of North Slope, Alaska, and offshore areas give a pessimistic interpretation of the situation. Comparing the FEA's business-as-usual figures with those of the Council on Energy Resources, the differences in the overall supply and demand forecast are great. Comparing either set of figures with those from the American Petroleum Institute results in still another interpretation.

Federal Energy Administration interpretation

One of the more difficult aspects of comparing any estimates of natural resources is understanding the terms that describe the resource situation. The FEA was required by the FEA Act of 1954 to prepare a complete and independent analysis of actual oil and gas reserves and resources in the United States and its Outer Continental Shelf. In that report FEA established three categories: (1) proved reserves, (2) indicated and inferred resources, and (3) undiscovered resources (fig. 9.10).

Proved reserves are the known reserves of crude oil, which represent the most definitive source for future production. The latest American Petroleum Institute survey of reserves estimated that proved oil reserves were 29.5 billion barrels (bbl) with most of the potential contained in Texas, Alaska, California, and Louisiana. This contrasts with reserves of 31.0 billion bbl at the start of 1977 and 32.7 billion bbl at the start of 1976, according to API.

Indicated reserves are those reserves as yet unproved but believed to be recoverable from known fields using known fluid injection techniques. According to the United States Geological Survey, they amount to 4.7 billion barrels. *Inferred reserves* are estimated by

10. Council on Energy Resources, *Overview*, May 11, 1977; *An Interim Overview*, September 12, 1977; and *National Energy Policy: A Continuing Assessment*, January, 1978 (Austin: The University of Texas at Austin).

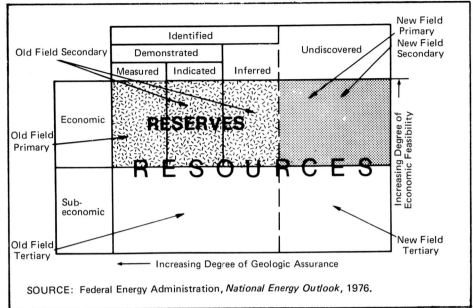

Figure 9.10. A diagrammatical explanation of the various categories of petroleum resources and reserves in the United States

calculating from demonstrated reserves and additional extensions, revisions, and new horizons within the defined limit of an oil field. USGS calculates inferred reserves amounting to 23 billion barrels.

Undiscovered resources are resources that the USGS thinks are probably recoverable. These undiscovered resources are usually estimated in percentages; for example, a statistical mean, or 50–50 chance of having more crude oil than the estimate or less crude oil than the estimate, was approximately 82 billion barrels of economically recoverable oil resources, according to USGS.

Even when the statistics are taken from similar sources, the conclusions vary considerably, depending upon the interpretation given them. The Council on Energy Resources' publication[11] cites criteria upon which to judge whether future production of gas and oil is likely to be as high as the FEA's estimates[12] would lead the nation to believe. One factor affecting future production is the relationship between the wellhead price of oil and gas and the industry's expenditures in exploration, development, and production. Oil drilling declined steadily from 1959 until 1972 because of decreased profitability of domestic production, which was attributed to rising costs and flat oil prices compared with cheap foreign oil, and because of lack of access to federal lands in OCS and Alaska. Both the FEA and the Council on Energy Resources agree that industry expenditure on exploration, development, and production closely parallels price and value of produced oil and natural gas.

Council on Energy Resources interpretation

11. *National Energy Policy: A Continuing Assessment*, 1978.
12. *National Energy Outlook*, 1976.

Another factor is whether increased drilling onshore is designed to explore new reserves or simply exploit already known reserves more fully. Examining statistics for exploratory or wildcat drilling and discoveries of new fields and reservoirs shows that drilling activity in 1977 was the highest since 1959. According to API, drilling activity in 1977 totaled 44,982 new wells, the highest level in any year since 1959, and reserve additions of nearly 160 million bbl of reserves were added by new field discoveries, the real measure of wildcatting.

However, when the figures are examined carefully, the main reason for the increase in reserves noted by API is that the categories that the figures represent were revised. Rather than representing only reserves that can be recovered using known fluid-injection techniques, the API figures reflect the transfer of reserves into the "proved" category (reserves that require improved recovery techniques) and into the "indicated added reserves" category (reserves that require enhanced recovery techniques). A spokesman for the American Association of Petroleum Geologists pointed out that the improved rate of drilling had certainly made some difference in the slower rate of declining reserves. He added that the difference was small enough to be caused by the result of "calculations alone." And, according to a Standard Oil Company of California spokesman, "the bulk of the reason for the trend is based on a revision of reserves figures, rather than new discoveries."[13] One major reason for the increase in reserve figures is that API included the reserves for Prudhoe Bay for the first time in their 1977 statistics, and it is noted in passing that including these figures would substantially change the rather pessimistic prognosis of the CER figures. However, the experts agree that the yearly decline in reserves is a trend not likely to be reversed, although higher price incentives do encourage increased drilling.

The petroleum industry's problem is that the new drilling is being done on land less likely to produce or in areas, such as offshore, where the expense of exploration is high and the rate of finding hydrocarbons is proportionately less than in the past. It has been estimated that, if the current healthy rate of drilling were continued, perhaps a billion barrels of oil a year might be added to the reserves. This figure would still mean that the total reserves were still going down. A spokesman for the Society of Exploration Geophysicists agreed with this general prognosis while he cautioned the public that there was a ten- to fifteen-year gap between seismic work and the beginnings of production. The United States does have oil reserves, but those that remain are likely to be expensive to produce.

13. *Oil and Gas Journal*, April 17, 1978.

Bibliography

Adelman, M. A. *The World Petroleum Market.* Baltimore: John Hopkins University Press, 1972.

Allvine, Fred C., and Patterson, James M. *Competition, LTD.: The Marketing of Gasoline.* Bloomington, Ind.: Indiana University Press, 1972.

American Petroleum Institute. *Primer of Oil and Gas Production.* Dallas: Production Department, American Petroleum Institute, 1976.

Amoco Chemicals Corporation. "Amoco Chemicals Corporation, Texas City Plant." Houston: Amoco Public and Government Affairs Department, 1974.

Amoco Chemicals Corporation. "Chocolate Bayou Plant, Alvin, Texas." Houston: Amoco Public and Government Affairs Department, 1974.

Askari, Hosseing, and Cummings, John Thomas. *Oil, OECD, and the Third World: A Vicious Triangle?* Austin: Center for Middle Eastern Studies, The University of Texas at Austin, 1978.

Baker, Ron. *A Primer of Oilwell Drilling.* 4th ed. Austin, Texas: Petroleum Extension Service, The University of Texas at Austin, 1979.

Berger, Bill D., and Anderson, Kenneth E. *Modern Petroleum—A Basic Primer of the Industry.* Tulsa: Petroleum Publishing Co., 1978.

Bland, William F., and Davidson, Robert L., co-editors. *Petroleum Processing Handbook.* New York: McGraw-Hill Book Co., 1967.

Burton, Dudley J. *The Governance of Energy: Problems, Prospects, and Underlying Issues.* New York: Praeger Publishers, 1980.

Council on Energy Resources. *An Interim Overview.* Austin, Texas: The University of Texas at Austin, 1977.

Council on Energy Resources. *National Energy Policy: A Continuing Assessment.* Austin, Texas: The University of Texas at Austin, 1978.

Council on Energy Resources. *Overview.* Austin, Texas: The University of Texas at Austin, 1977.

Dell'Osso, Juino, Jr. "Algeria II LNG Project Plans Detailed." *Oil and Gas Journal,* May 29, 1978.

Dobrin, Milton Burnett. *Introduction to Geophysical Prospecting,* 3rd ed. New York: McGraw-Hill Book Co., 1976.

Eckbo, Paul Leo. *The Future of World Oil.* Cambridge: Ballinger Publishing Co., 1976.

Federal Energy Administration. *National Energy Outlook, 1976.* Washington, D.C.: Government Printing Office, 1976.

Fischer, Joel D., and Fliakos, Constantine D. *British Petroleum: A Basic Report.* New York: Drexel Burnham Lambert, Inc., 1978.

Fried, Edward R., and Schultze, Charles L., co-editors. *Higher Oil Prices and the World Economy: The Adjustment Problem.* Washington, D.C.: The Brookings Institution, 1975.

Guthrie, Virgil B., ed. *Petroleum Products Handbook.* New York: McGraw-Hill Book Co., 1960.

Mangan, Frank. *The Pipeliners.* El Paso: Guynes Press, 1977.

Maurizi, Alex, and Kelly, Thom. *Prices and Consumer Information: The Benefits from Posting Retail Gasoline Prices.* Washington, D.C.: American Enterprise Institute for Public Policy Research, 1978.

Moses, Leslie. "From Lease to Release." *AAPL Guide for Landmen.* Fort Worth, Texas: American Association of Petroleum Landmen, 1970.

Natural Gas from Overseas, Columbia Gas System, April, 1978.

"The Natural Gas Pipeline Industry." Washington, D.C.

Odell, Peter R. *Oil and World Power.* New York: Penguin Books, 1979.

Our Magnificent Earth: A Rand McNally Atlas of Earth Resources. New York: Rand McNally & Co., 1979.

Petroleum Extension Service. *Rotary Drilling Series, Units I, II, III, and V.* Austin, Texas: The University of Texas at Austin.

Petroleum Extension Service. *Well Service and Workover Series, Lessons 1–12.* Austin, Texas: The University of Texas at Austin.

Petty, O. Scott. *Seismic Reflections.* Houston: Geosource Inc., 1976.

Rostow, W. W.; Fisher, William L.; and Kozmetsky, George. "The National Energy Plan: An Overview." *Preliminary Assessment of the President's National Energy Plan.* Austin: The University of Texas at Austin, 1977.

Stephens, Maynard M., and Spencer, Oscar F. *Petroleum and Natural Gas Production.* University Park, Pa.: Pennsylvania State University, 1957.

Stockil, P. A., ed. *Our Industry Petroleum.* London: British Petroleum Co., Ltd., 1977.

Telford, W. M., et al. *Applied Geophysics.* Cambridge and New York: Cambridge University Press, 1976.